Cornelia Veltema

John
Deere

Blacksmith Boy

Illustrated by Robert Doremus

John
Deere

Blacksmith Boy

By Margaret Ann Bare

Macmillan Publishing Company
New York

Macmillan Publishing Company
866 Third Avenue, New York, NY 10022

Printed in the United States of America

First Edition

10   9   8   7   6   5   4   3

Library of Congress Catalog Card Number: 64-24808
ISBN: 0-02-708381-0

*To my mother
in loving memory of my father,
Worthy A. Matthews,
whose lifework also benefited
the prairie farmers*

With sincere appreciation and gratitude I wish to acknowledge the invaluable assistance of Mrs. Caldwell R. Rosborough, Moline, Illinois, in gathering research material for this book about the childhood of her great-uncle, John Deere.

I am also grateful for the excellent cooperation and assistance of Deere & Company. Especially do I wish to thank Mr. George F. Neiley, Jr., Director of Public Relations; Mr. Roger J. Fritz, Secretary of John Deere Foundation; and Mrs. Charlotte L. Anderson, Librarian.

For their help with the authentication of the Vermont chapters, I wish to thank Mr. and Mrs. Worth Shampeny, Rochester, Vermont, and Mrs. William Burrage, Middlebury, Vermont.

For supplying the initial impetus which led to the writing of this biography, I wish to thank Mr. Marlin Baxter, Director of Curriculum, Moline Public Schools, Moline, Illinois.

Illustrations

Numerous smaller illustrations

Contents

★ # John
Deere

Blacksmith Boy

Muscles Count

John was worried. Where was Seth? Why didn't he come? This was their last day to play! Tomorrow was Sunday, and no one could play on the Sabbath! Monday school began!

On the bridge just above the waterfalls, John Deere, a nine-year-old boy with light wavy hair and blue eyes, was waiting for his friend, Seth Miller. It was ten o'clock. On this September day in the year 1813 the sun was already hot in Middlebury, Vermont.

"School!" John mumbled to himself. "Who wants to go to school when there are so many things to do outdoors?" He leaned over the rail-

11

ing and watched the waters of Otter Creek go roaring over the falls.

"Hi, there, John!" Seth came running across the bridge. He was out of breath. "I had to pick —two baskets of peaches—before I could leave. Have you been waiting long?"

"Oh, about fifteen minutes, I guess," John admitted. "I was afraid you weren't coming."

A team of brown horses pulling a carriage rattled past. The boys stepped closer to the bridge railing and leaned over.

"Look! There goes a big log over the falls!" John exclaimed. "Let's see if we can hit it before it gets by!"

Both boys found stones on the bridge floor. Seth threw and John threw. They missed. John got another stone.

"That log's too far away now," Seth decided.

"No it's not!" John insisted. Back went his arm. Away went the stone.

Kerplunk! It hit the log!

"Golly, you sure can throw far, John!" Seth said admiringly.

"Oh, I come here and practice a lot," John replied modestly. He lived on Main Street close to the south end of the bridge. "Let's get going, Seth. Let's see how far we can follow Otter Creek. We'll pretend we're explorers."

Just then a team of black horses pulling a farm wagon clattered up onto the bridge.

"That's my Uncle Amos coming!" Seth shouted and waved at the driver.

"Whoa, Dolly! Whoa, Prince!" Amos Miller pulled back on the reins. "You boys want to ride over to Captain Lawrence's blacksmith shop with me?" he asked. "Get in if you do. Prince, there, needs a new shoe!"

"You bet! We'd like to go!" John accepted for both of them. The boys climbed up over the big wheel and into the back of the wagon.

13

"Giddyap!" Uncle Amos shook the reins and the horses started on again. The wagon jolted across the bridge and on down Main Street.

John's eyes were sparkling. It was fun to ride in a wagon, but it was even more exciting to go to the blacksmith shop! He'd rather watch Captain Lawrence even than go down Otter Creek. Anyway, the shop was right along the Creek. They could still go exploring.

Even before the wagon stopped, they could hear the loud clang! clang! of the blacksmith's hammer on the anvil.

Uncle Amos unhitched the horses. He looped Dolly's reins over a hitching rail and led Prince toward the wide door of the shop. "Now you lads stay out of the way," he warned as the boys followed him inside. "You can get hurt here."

Down came the blacksmith's hammer. Clang! Sparks flew from the red-hot iron which Captain Lawrence held on the anvil with a pair of tongs.

14

Clang! He was bending the iron to make another link in a heavy chain.

What strong arms and big muscles the blacksmith had! John watched him admiringly.

Clang! Clang! Now the two ends of the link were joined together. Captain Lawrence lifted the chain with his long-handled tongs and plunged it into a tub of water.

SSSSSssssssst! Steam rose and hissed. When the iron had turned black and the steam was gone, he raised the chain from the tub and hung it over an iron peg on the wall.

Captain Lawrence rubbed his hands on his leather apron and grinned at the boys. "I see you brought me a couple of helpers, Amos."

"Yep, Captain, so I did! Thought you and I could go down to the creek and fish while these lads put a shoe on old Prince!" The men and the boys laughed. All of them knew John and Seth couldn't shoe a horse.

It was fun to watch, though. First, Captain Lawrence held Prince's foot between his knees and trimmed the hoof with a sharp knife.

"Doesn't that hurt Prince?" Seth asked.

"No more than it hurts you to have your toenails cut," the Captain answered.

"But when you nail the shoe on, that will hurt, won't it?" Seth was still doubtful.

"No, lad, that won't hurt Prince either. You watch, and you'll see that I drive the nails just through the horny part of his hoof," the smith explained.

While Seth asked his questions, John had been looking at the blacksmith's tools. There were big hammers that looked too heavy to lift. There were small hammers with round ends. There were sharp-pointed chisels and tongs of all sizes. Across wooden beams overhead were long bars and rods of iron. John wished he could use some of those tools.

John stepped closer to the forge where the coals of a hot fire burned. He liked the smell of the burning coke. He was sure he would like to make useful things from hot iron.

Many horseshoes hung over a pole along one side of the shop. Captain Lawrence took one of these down. He held it against Prince's hoof and scratched a mark on it with a nail.

"I'll have to make this one a bit longer," he said. With the long-handled tongs he pushed the ends of the horseshoe deep into the bed of hot coals. John watched with interest.

"John," the captain called, "work the bellows for me. You've got strong arms, boy!"

John took hold of a long wooden handle that stuck out beside the forge. As he pulled it down, the big sack, or bellows, behind the forge squeezed shut and pushed air up through the fire. The flames burned upward, hot and bright. When the handle went up, the bellows filled

17

with air. When the handle came down, the air blew through the fire and made it glow and blaze. John liked the sound of the air whistling through the bellows.

Soon Prince's new shoe was hot enough to be bent and pounded into shape. Captain Lawrence took the glowing iron from the fire with his tongs and turned and hammered it on his anvil. When it was the right size for Prince, he quickly stuck it into the water tub. Cooling the iron made it harden again.

When the shoe was cold, Captain Lawrence lifted Prince's hoof between his knees. Using flat-headed horseshoe nails, he carefully nailed the shoe to the horny part of the hoof.

Prince stood quietly. He seemed to like getting a new shoe. The boys knew he hadn't been hurt at all.

Captain Lawrence patted Prince. "You're a fine fellow, Prince. I wish all horses stood as quietly as you do."

The blacksmith walked to the door with Uncle Amos and the two boys as they led Prince outside to hitch him to the wagon.

"Amos," he said, "I'd a lot rather shoe Prince than Dolly over there. She's a nervous one."

"Yes, Captain, Dolly's afraid of most everything. She's a good worker, though," Uncle Amos replied as he walked Prince toward the hitching rail where Dolly was tied.

"Good-by, Captain Lawrence. Good-by, Uncle Amos. John and I are going to hike down along the creek. Race you down there, John!" Seth waved to the men and ran down the path.

John waited a moment, patting Dolly's and Prince's soft noses.

"Thanks for the ride, Mr. Miller," he said. "Thanks for letting me work the bellows, Captain Lawrence!"

Just then a yellow cat streaked around the corner of the shop, followed by a wildly barking dog. They ran right between Dolly's front legs. The mare snorted, reared, and plunged backward. The reins pulled loose from the rail and she started to run. John jumped and grabbed the reins near her head. He hung on.

"Whoa, Dolly, whoa!" he shouted and pulled with all his might. Dolly danced and threw her head up. John held on tightly, although he was lifted right off the ground!

Then Captain Lawrence was there. He pulled Dolly's head down and made her stand still. John could let go now.

Uncle Amos ran toward John. "Are you hurt, boy?" he asked.

"No, sir. I'm all right."

Captain Lawrence patted John on the back. "Good work, lad!" he said. "You've a quick wit and strong muscles. You saved Amos from having a runaway horse today!"

John felt proud as he ran to catch up with Seth. He thought of what his mother had said at breakfast. "Eat every bit of your oatmeal, John. It will make you big and strong."

He thought of what his older brother, Francis had said last night. "You are a good worker, John. Carrying water and wood for mother makes you both helpful and strong."

They were right. John resolved that from now on he would look for more hard work that would not only help the family but make him strong. Throwing stones helped, too! It really paid to have strong arms and muscles.

The Hornets' Nest

THE TWO boys followed the path along Otter Creek. They saw two squirrels chasing each other around the trunk of a big maple tree.

They stopped to watch a blue kingfisher bird swoop down to the water and fly away with a minnow. As they rounded a little bend in the path, they heard a loud scurrying noise from the bushes just ahead.

They stopped and listened.

There it was again. Something was moving in those bushes!

"John," whispered Seth, "do you think it could be a bear in there?"

"No. There aren't any bears here. Bears don't come this close to town."

"Sometimes they do—if they're hungry!"

"Well, they're not hungry now. The woods are full of berries and nuts."

"Maybe he's after some berries around here! Maybe we'd better go back, John. We've come pretty far. It's pretty wild here."

Just then the bushes parted and a small, black furry head appeared, sniffing at the ground. The animal did not see the boys.

Seth and John stood very still. They could tell it wasn't a bear, but what was it?

The little animal raised its head and walked out into the path.

It was a skunk! The sun shone through the trees on its pretty black fur with the white stripe down the back.

The boys didn't make a sound. They didn't want the skunk to think they were enemies!

While they were watching it anxiously, the skunk looked up the path. Then it looked down the path. It saw the boys. It turned its head to one side and then the other.

"Are these boys friends?" it seemed to be asking. "Is it safe with them here?"

Finally the skunk turned and started up the path. Then it stopped and made a low crying sound and looked toward the bushes.

Out from under the bushes marched four baby skunks, one after the other! They looked like black and white kittens! With their little tails curling over their backs, they followed their mother up the path.

John and Seth didn't move. When the skunk family was out of sight, the boys sat down on a big rock and laughed.

"They were so dignified," John chuckled. "They looked just like a parade."

"Well, for a while there, when the mother

skunk was looking at us, I almost wished she was a bear!" Seth was thinking what his mother would have said if he and John had come home smelling like a skunk!

John was staring up into the branches of a big maple tree.

"Look, Seth. There's a big hornets' nest!" He looked up and pointed to a large, egg-shaped gray object hanging from a limb about twenty feet above their heads.

"Do you think there are hornets in it?" Seth asked. "Let's get away if there are!"

"I don't see any flying around. Do you?" John squinted his eyes as he looked up into the tree. "Listen! Do you hear any?"

The boys were quiet. They heard a woodpecker tapping. They heard a fish splash in the creek. But they didn't hear any buzzing sound. They approached cautiously.

"Let's see if we can knock it down," John

suggested. He began looking around for a long stick and finally found a straight branch.

"Maybe those hornets are just taking a nap!" Seth said doubtfully. He knew hornets were more dangerous than skunks.

"My mother would like to have that hornets' nest," John said, as he pulled the long stick from a pile of brush.

Seth looked surprised. "Why would your mother want an old hornets' nest?"

"'Cause it's good for Betsey's throat," John explained. Betsey was John's ten-year-old sister. He held the stick up under the nest. It was too short. He could only touch the nest.

"Does she have to eat a hornets' nest?" Seth swallowed. His stomach felt queer just thinking about it.

John laughed as he threw the stick down and began looking for another. "No, silly, she doesn't eat it! Mother mashes it up into a wet paste. Then she puts it on Betsey's neck with a soft cloth over it."

Seth felt better. "Guess I'd rather have hornet-nest-mud on my neck than that smelly old salt pork and vinegar! That's what Mother put on me last winter!"

Soon the boys found a longer stick. This one was long enough, but the end was so small that it wasn't strong enough. They took turns hitting the hornets' nest. The stick just bent. The nest didn't even budge!

"My arms are getting tired," Seth complained. "Those old hornets sure know how to glue their house on a branch!"

"Yep," John answered, as he jumped and struck again. "Even bad windstorms won't blow them down. Old hornets' nests stay in the trees and bushes for years."

"You're not going to get that nest down, John. Let's go on!" Seth wanted to quit.

"No, I'm not giving up yet! There must be some way to get it down," John insisted. He dropped the long stick, put his hands on his hips, and stared up at the nest.

"I know! I've got it!" John's blue eyes sparkled. He ran down to the edge of the creek and began picking up rocks.

"What are you going to do, John? What do you want rocks for? Think you can knock it down with a rock? Think you can throw hard enough?" Seth had caught John's excitement.

"Maybe I can," John replied. "I'm going to try, anyway. It might work."

John threw and Seth threw. Sometimes they hit. Sometimes they missed. They made dents and a couple of holes in the nest, but it would not come down!

"At least we know there are no hornets up there," John said as he threw another rock.

Seth gave up. "Oh, let the old nest stay

there," he said. "I'm hungry. Let's eat our lunch. I'm tired of throwing rocks."

He sat down on a fallen log. Out of his shirt pocket he took two crumpled ginger cookies. Out of his pants pocket he pulled a red and yellow apple and polished it carefully.

John kept throwing rocks. The big ones wouldn't go high enough, and the smaller ones wouldn't budge the hornets' nest.

"Oh, stop it, John! Forget about the nest." Seth was even tired of watching. "Aren't you hungry?" he asked hopefully.

Finally John sat down beside his friend. He had an apple, too, and two pieces of cold, fried mush wrapped in brown paper.

"Let's go wading in the creek now," Seth said as he threw away his apple core.

John had been looking at the nest all the time he was eating. He hated to give up! He just couldn't let that old hornets' nest beat him!

"If we could just bend that big branch down a ways——" he began. Suddenly he jumped up and ran over to the trunk of the big maple.

Seth went, too. "The tree's too big to climb. I thought of that. There are no branches down here to get hold of. Come on. Let's go wading. It'll be time to go home pretty soon."

"I'm not going to climb it, Seth. But see this wild grapevine growing up the trunk? Help me pull it down."

"What for?"

"You'll see. Just pull."

Soon the boys had the long grapevine on the ground. The big end of the vine was rooted near the trunk of the maple tree.

John picked up the small, loose end of the vine and wrapped it around and around a flat rock. Then he fished a piece of string from his pocket. He tied the string tightly around and around the vine and rock.

32

"What are you going to do?" Seth was puzzled. "What good is the grapevine? It won't knock that nest down!"

"No," John answered, "but if I can throw this stone with the vine on it over that branch, we can pull the nest down far enough to hit it! I know we can!"

John stepped back. He aimed carefully. Up went the stone, and the vine zigzagged after it! Down came the stone on the other side of the branch! Both boys shouted.

They ran over. They could reach the vine! Perhaps they could reach the nest!

"Easy!" John warned. "We'll have to pull this end carefully, till we can get hold of the heavy part of the vine!"

Slowly the boys pulled. At last they had the tough, wooden vine in their hands. Now they pulled harder. The branch began to bend. Down, down, came the big limb.

"I can hold it!" John puffed. "You let go, Seth, and see if you can knock off the nest! Get that stick!"

Seth grabbed a big stick. Yes, he could reach it Now he was as eager as John.

Whack! Whack! Whack! Down it came!

"Hooray! Hooray!" both boys shouted.

A little later the two boys were standing in the kitchen of John's home. His mother was holding the smooth, paper-like hornets' nest in her hands. She smiled down at the two warm, dusty boys. They had forgotten all about wading in the creek. They had raced home immediately to show her their prize.

"John just wouldn't give up, Mrs. Deere," Seth finished telling the story. "He wouldn't. He just had to have that nest for you!"

"John must have remembered how a hornets' nest plaster helped Betsey's quinsy last winter." Mrs. Deere patted John's shoulder.

"I'm glad he remembered," she went on. "Nests like this are hard to find. This is the biggest one I've ever seen. I'm surely happy to get it. It will be useful next winter."

John felt good. His mother was pleased. He liked to see her smile. This last year she had so often looked sad. Right now she looked happy. He was glad he had won the battle with that old nest! He was glad he hadn't given up.

"It pays to keep trying," he said to himself. Suddenly his good feeling left, because his mother added, "If John will try just as hard to get his lessons for Master Hoyt this winter, as he did to get this nest, I'll be even happier. I know he can do well if he studies."

"Lessons!" John mumbled, looking down at the floor. "Monday morning—school!"

Now the whole world seemed gloomy. It was as though the sun had gone under a cloud! John dreaded the long, tiresome hours sitting on a school bench. He hated staying indoors all day and puzzling over words and numbers!

This had been such a fine day, spent visiting the blacksmith shop and finding the hornets' nest. Now it was spoiled because he had to think of school again!

"Cheer up, John!" Mrs. Deere was still smiling. "You and Seth can have some of these fresh doughnuts and a glass of milk."

But even the sweet, golden-brown doughnuts and the cool milk couldn't make John happy again. Tomorrow he would have to spend the day in the gloomy schoolroom.

He sighed as he said to Seth, "I wish summer was just starting! Guess I'll never be happy as long as I have to go to school!"

The Rabbit's Foot

"COME-TO-SCHOOOOL! Come-to-schoool!"

John woke up. Who was calling him to school? Then he heard it again.

"Cock-a-doodle-do! Cock-a-doodle-do!"

It was only Mr. Kellogg's old red rooster!

John smiled. He remembered it was only Sunday! That old rooster was wrong!

"Wake up, George! Wake up! I can smell the bacon frying!" John reached over and playfully spanked his six-year-old brother, who was sleeping beside him.

George sat up in bed and rubbed his eyes.

"Is today Monday?" he asked sleepily.

George was happy that school was starting. He could go for the first time this year. He would be in the first grade.

John jumped out of bed. He scowled at his brother. "How can you want to go to school? Well, I guess you're too young to know any better!" His face brightened. "Today is the Sabbath, George. You can go to meeting."

"No! I want to go to real school!" George sounded cross. He looked as if he might cry. That would never do on Sunday morning. Mother would be upset. On the Sabbath everyone was supposed to be quiet and thoughtful and especially kind to everyone else.

"I'll take you to school tomorrow, George," John promised. "Look! I'm almost dressed! If you hurry, I'll wait and tie your shoes."

George tumbled out of bed, grabbed his clothes, and started to dress. The night before their mother had neatly laid out on two chairs the boys' white shirts, black stockings, and good pants. The boys went downstairs to the kitchen where their mother was working.

"Good morning, boys," she greeted them when they took their places at the large round kitchen table. Sarah Deere, a tall, pretty woman, with light brown hair combed back into a smooth roll, looked as neat as a pin in her blue Sunday dress and crisp white apron.

Soon Betsey and the two older boys, Francis, 14, and William, 12, came to breakfast. When the children were seated, Mrs. Deere took her place between George and John.

All of them folded their hands and bowed their heads. It was Betsey's turn to say the blessing.

For our daily bread, O Lord,
Make us truly thankful.
For all the blessings Thou hast sent
We are truly grateful. Amen.

Even before Betsey said "Amen," George's brown curly head popped up. "You didn't close your eyes, William!" he shouted gleefully. "Your eyes were open the whole time while Betsey was saying the blessing!"

"Now, how could you tell that, George, if your eyes were shut?" asked William.

"Well——" George hesitated. "Well, anyway I had only one eye open!"

All the children laughed. Mrs. Deere smiled at her youngest. Then she said seriously, "We must always close our eyes when we pray, boys. That makes it easier to think about our blessings. George, you musn't talk so loudly. It isn't polite. Besides, it's the Sabbath, you know."

George nodded his head. "I like Betsey's blessing better than yours, William," he whispered loudly. "Yours is too long!"

The children all wanted to please their mother. They knew how hard she worked making dresses and capes and coats for other people. They knew how much she missed their father, too. It was only a little more than a year ago that their father had died. His name had been William, too.

He had been a tailor. The front part of their house had been his tailoring shop. There he had made fine woolen suits and coats. Last year he had sailed on the Atlantic Ocean to England to buy woolen cloth, but he had not come back. He had died during the trip.

Mrs. Deere now worked alone in the tailoring shop. The children helped all they could. Francis cut the heavy woolen cloth where his mother had marked it. William often delivered a fine new coat or cape to its owner. Betsey swept the floor of the shop, trimmed the large candles or sewing dips, and kept the work tables neat and orderly. John was always glad to do errands for his mother. She often sent him to the store to buy thread or buttons or hooks. Even little George helped. He wound yarn into balls and filled the scrap box with left-over pieces of cloth.

When all of them were ready for church, Mrs. Deere smiled her approval. "My, how fine my children look!" she said.

The boys, their hair neatly combed, stood very straight. Their coats had been brushed and pressed, and their shoes had been cleaned and shined. Betsey's long white dress didn't have a single wrinkle. Her curls were brushed into long rolls, and her bonnet was tied beneath her chin with a blue ribbon.

"I wish we had a carriage and a horse so we could ride to church," Betsey said.

"Why, Betsey Deere! What a lazy thing to say!" scolded William. "You ought to be glad the Meeting House is so close! We can walk quicker than we could harness a horse!"

"I'm going to have a team of six black horses when I grow up!" George announced.

"Now, children, that's enough," Mrs. Deere said firmly, but kindly. "Come, Betsey, you walk with me. Then John and William. Francis, you'd better take hold of George's hand. George, today I don't want Mr. Mills to have to tickle you even once!"

Mr. Mills was the tithingman. He stood in the back of the Meeting House with his long stick or wand. On the end of the wand was a rabbit's foot. If any child fell asleep, whispered, or even wiggled too much, Mr. Mills came down the aisle and ticked him. A child who had to be tickled was disgraced.

The Deere family walked over the bridge and up Main Street. They passed Merchants' Row, where all the stores were tightly closed. They went along Park Court Square, where farmers, who brought their families to church in wagons and carriages, had tied their horses to the hitching posts.

The big white Meeting House with its tall steeple, was just across from the park. The Deere family followed Francis up the steps and into the church. Mr. Mills was standing just inside with his wand.

"I do hope George will sit still and not whisper today!" John said to himself. He followed Betsey, his mother, and George into their pew. William sat beside John, and Francis sat next to the aisle of the cool, quiet church. Sunshine streamed through the open windows and made leafy patterns on the polished dark wood of the pews.

When Seth came in with his family, he turned and grinned at John. After a quick nod, John didn't look at Seth again. The boys might begin to laugh if they continued to look at each other for very long.

44

John watched Pastor Merrill. The pastor, in his long black coat, went up the stairs into the high wooden pulpit at the front of the church. When he raised his arms, everyone stood up. Then he began to pray. John closed his eyes and tried to listen. Soon, however, he began to think about the blacksmith shop.

After the long prayer, the congregation sang a hymn. John loved to sing. He liked the singing better than any other part of the church service.

George liked the singing, too. He didn't have to be quiet then. He could tap his feet and drum his fingers on the wood. He watched his brother and tried to sing the same words his brother sang.

Come we that love the Lord,
And let our joys be known;
Join in a song with sweet accord,
And thus surround His throne.

"—His throne!" George finished loudly, after everyone else had stopped singing.

Mrs. Deere looked down at him and frowned. Francis, glancing down at his small brother, shook his head. Betsey and William stared straight ahead. John flushed and looked down at his shoes. He wished he weren't sitting next to George.

Then Pastor Merrill began to preach, and John tried to listen to the sermon. Pastor Merrill used such big words! John looked out the window and saw a bluejay flash through the branches of an elm tree.

Then John noticed that his mother seemed upset. First she looked at George, then at the floor, then at George again.

John saw that his little brother was quietly playing the church game with his fingers. First George locked his fingers. Then he made a steeple with his first two fingers and the church

46

doors with his thumbs. Then he opened his thumbs and quickly turned his hands over so all the fingers pointed up.

John could remember when he used to do the same thing. He knew that George was saying to himself,

Here's the church
And here's the steeple.
Open the door
And see all the people!

John looked at his mother again. Her eyes were open very wide. Again she glanced, first at George, then at the floor under his feet, then back at John.

At first John didn't see anything when he looked at the floor. Then he looked more intently, and his eyes got bigger too!

There, close to George's feet, was a little brown tree toad! John knew the toad would jump before long!

John saw that his mother's eyes looked softer now. She glanced again at George. Then she gave John a tiny nod which he understood.

George loved frogs and toads. If he saw this one, he'd surely forget he was in church. He'd probably yell right out loud!

Mother wanted John to get rid of the toad before George saw it. How could he do it without his little brother noticing? For a minute John sat very still and thought. Then he reached into his coat pocket and got out his white Sunday handkerchief.

Out of the corner of his eye, he saw Mr. Mills moving slowly down their side of the church. John looked down at George. The boy was starting to lock his fingers again. John knew he had to try. He took a deep breath and put his handkerchief over his mouth.

"Ka-chew!" He pretended to sneeze. As he did so he bent over as far as he could. When

48

he straightened up, he had scooped the little toad into his handkerchief.

People turned their heads to look at him. John felt his neck getting hot. Quickly he put the handkerchief into his pocket.

Thump! Tickle! Tickle! Mr. Mills was rubbing the rabbit's foot over John's cheek.

John stared straight ahead. He felt as if his face was burning up! He wanted to get up and run out of the Meeting House!

He was the first one home from church. He hadn't even waited to talk with Seth. When the rest of the family came in, George began to chant, "John got the rabbit's foot! John got the rabbit's foot!"

Mrs. Deere grabbed her youngest son. She knelt in front of him. "George Deere! You stop that teasing this minute!"

"Why, Mother? John was bad! He sneezed too hard. I was good. Mr. Mills told me I behaved very well."

"John was not bad. John was good. That was a necessary sneeze!" Mrs. Deere looked at John over George's head. There were tears in her eyes, but she was smiling. Betsey, Francis, and William looked puzzled.

Their mother stood up, walked over to John,

and put her arm around his shoulders. "I'm proud of John," she told them all. "He did a fine thing today, and he did it for you, George! Show them why you sneezed, son."

John took out his handkerchief, unfolded it, and showed them the toad.

"A toad! A little old tree toad!" George yelled delightedly.

"Yes!" Mrs. Deere laughed. "That's just how you would have sounded in church, George, if John hadn't sneezed and caught the toad."

George stroked the little animal with one finger. "How can you catch a toad by sneezing?" he wanted to know.

"It's a trick!" John told his brother. He could laugh now, too. The rabbit's foot didn't matter any more. His mother was proud of him, and that was all that really mattered.

The Fly

JOHN PEELED the red and white paper from the point of his new slate pencil. Half of the first day of school was over. So far, it really hadn't been a bad day.

Master Hoyt had told them about the war in Europe. He related how most of Napoleon's army had frozen to death in Russia last winter. The story was exciting, but terrible.

Now England was fighting Napoleon! The English were stopping American ships and taking off our sailors to fight in their war! That wasn't fair! It was why the United States was at war with England.

52

John, who was supposed to be working his arithmetic problems, saw Master Hoyt looking at him. The boy looked down at his book and read the first problem.

A stage arrived with eight passengers. Five got out. Four new passengers got on. How many passengers were on the stage when it left?

Carefully John wrote on his slate: 8—5=3. Then he wrote: 3+4— Just then a fly lighted on his desk. John watched the fly climb up his arithmetic book and walk across the page.

"Bet you can't catch it!" Willie Baker, who was also watching the fly, whispered. Willie sat beside him at the big double desk.

John glanced up at Master Hoyt. The schoolmaster was not looking at the two boys. He was helping the first class count beans.

"Bet I can!" John whispered back. He waited until the fly was in the middle of the page. Then

—*Zip!* His right hand moved like lightning! The fly was in his fist! John looked at Willie and grinned.

"Lucky!" Willie hissed, just a little too loudly. Several children glanced at the two boys. Master Hoyt raised his head and looked about the room. John and Willie bent their heads over their slates and pretended to study.

John tried to pick up his slate pencil, but he couldn't without letting the fly go. Keeping his head bent, he put both hands in his lap. Opening his fist just a little, he got the fly between his left thumb and forefinger. Then with his thumbnail he pinched off one of the fly's wings.

Gently he laid the fly on his slate. It whirled around and around. It couldn't fly. He began to feel sorry for it.

"Guess I'd better kill that old fly," he said to himself.

"John Deere! Stand up!" Master Hoyt's voice was loud and sharp.

John was startled. He almost jumped out of his seat. He saw his sister Betsey and the other children look up in alarm.

"Young man, have you finished your lesson?"

"No, sir."

"How many problems have you done?"

"N-none, sir."

"Do you find them too difficult?"

"No, sir."

"Kindly explain, then, why you have failed to do even one!"

"I-I caught a fly, Master Hoyt."

Several boys snickered and a girl giggled. The teacher rapped on his desk with his wooden pointer. "Bring me the fly," he commanded.

John picked up the fly and walked to the front of the room. He was glad Francis and William were in the classroom across the hall.

As he passed Betsey's desk he saw that she looked frightened. He laid the fly, which was still whirling helplessly, on Master Hoyt's desk. The schoolmaster watched the fly for a moment. Then he leaned forward and looked straight at John. The boy looked down at the floor.

"This fly has only one wing. It that why you were able to catch it?"

John wanted very badly to say, "Yes." But it wasn't the truth. It would be a lie.

His throat felt dry. He swallowed and then said quickly, "No, sir. It had two wings when I caught it. I—I snipped one off so it couldn't fly. I was watching it."

"So!" Master Hoyt straightened and brought the pointer from behind his back. "So! You admit that you were torturing a poor insect rather than doing your lessons?"

"Y-yes, sir." John hung his head. Out of the corner of his eye he saw George at the beginners' bench. His little brother was staring, wide-eyed and open-mouthed. Betsey might not tell Mother, but George would.

John could just imagine George running in to Mother, shouting, "John got a flogging! On the first day of school, too!"

Master Hoyt shook his pointer at John. "Young man, do you know what I should do to you?" he asked.

"Y-yes, sir."

"Turn around then, and tell your classmates. Tell them why I should do it."

As John slowly turned and faced the room he could feel his face getting hot and red. He looked down at the floor.

"I—I——" he gulped. Then he went on hurriedly, "I should have a flogging for not doing my lessons and for hurting the fly!"

"Exactly!" Master Hoyt agreed. He rapped on the desk with his pointer.

"Come here, John," he commanded.

John's heart beat faster. His legs felt weak. Betsey's and George's faces stood out among all those staring at him.

"I won't cry!" he said to himself. "No matter how it hurts, I won't cry!"

Master Hoyt reached out and brushed the fly off his desk. "Kill that poor insect," he said. "Flies carry dirt. They should be killed, but never tortured."

John tapped the fly with his shoe. He kept looking at it to avoid having to face his classmates in that quiet room.

"Yes, you deserve a whipping," the teacher continued, "but I am going to spare you this time. First, because you were honest. Second, because there is something you need more than a flogging. You need to learn a lesson that you will not forget.

John looked up in surprise as Master Hoyt

picked up a spelling book and turned several pages. He handed the open book to John.

"On this page," he said, "are the Rules for a Good Boy. Go to your seat and memorize Rules Seven and Nine. Before school is dismissed you will stand before the class and recite those rules. Think about what you are learning."

John took the book and started back to his desk. Then he stopped, turned to the schoolmaster and said, "Thank you, sir."

As John slid into his seat, Willie said under his breath, "Lucky!"

John didn't answer. He didn't even look at Willie. He put the book on the desk and began to read attentively.

He didn't hear George counting his beans. He didn't notice when Seth went up to the big blackboard to work a problem. He didn't even look up when Master Hoyt rang the little bell for the pupils to go out and play.

He read the rules over and over. He practiced saying the first line to himself. Then he shut his eyes and tried to say the second line. When he had learned that, he went on to the third line. Finally he could say all of Rule Seven without looking at the book. Then he began on Rule Nine.

"John. John Deere!" The schoolmaster had to say his name twice before John heard and looked up from the book.

"Yes, sir?"

"We are waiting for you to recite, John." Master Hoyt's voice was kind now.

John looked about the room. All the other pupils had their books neatly piled on top of their slates. They had folded their hands on their desks. They were ready to go home.

John walked to the front of the room. He turned and faced the class. He took a deep breath and began to recite.

"Rule Seven. A good boy is kind even to dumb creatures such as beasts, birds, fishes, insects and worms. He knows that, though they cannot speak, they can feel as well as he."

"Good," nodded Master Hoyt. "Now recite Rule Nine."

John continued, "A good boy never takes delight in catching flies, or other insects, nor in ——" John hesitated. He could feel his face starting to get hot again. But he looked up and finished clearly, "nor in pulling off their wings or legs because he thinks it cruel to torture them and give them pain."

"And do you think so?" asked the teacher.

"Yes, sir. I won't do it again," he promised. "I didn't think before."

Master Hoyt stepped forward and put his hand on John's shoulder.

"Young ladies and gentlemen," he said to the class, "I hope all of you have learned something from John today. I hope you have learned that all living creatures have feelings. I hope you have seen that honesty is always the best policy. I hope, also, that John has shown you how quickly you can learn when you keep your mind on your work."

Later, as they were walking home, George looked up at John and asked, "Master Hoyt was pretty mean to you today, wasn't he?"

John shook his head. "No, he wasn't mean. He was fair, George. I did a wrong thing and he made me learn what was right. I think I'll like going to school to Master Hoyt."

A Task and a Trip

"JOHN, WILL YOU please polish this needle?" Mrs. Deere asked. "I can hardly get it through this heavy cloth."

It was February, 1814. John, Betsey, and George were helping their mother in the tailoring shop after school. It was cold outside, and the ground was covered with deep snow. But the shop was cozy and warm.

There was the good smell of pine burning in the fireplace and of beans baking in the kitchen oven.

John stopped turning the flax winder. He took the needle from his mother and found the little red cloth strawberry in her work table. The strawberry was filled with emery powder, which would polish the needles.

John pushed the needle rapidly in and out, in and out of the strawberry. At last it seemed smooth. To make sure, he tested it through a scrap of cloth.

"I think it will sew fine now, Mother," he said as he gave it back to her.

"Thank you, John," his mother answered. "Why, it looks just like a new needle! Now I can sew much faster than I have been doing. It won't be long before I have this cape and hood finished for Mrs. Miller."

"Do you have any more needles that need polishing?" John asked hopefully. He liked to polish needles better than to wind thread.

Mrs. Deere took a pink silk needle case from the table drawer, "Here are all my needles, John. Some of them are very small. Be careful not to lose any," she warned. "Steel needles are expensive, you know. They have to be sent all the way from England."

Betsey looked up from her sewing. "Master Hoyt says nothing comes from England now."

"That's right, Betsey," her mother agreed. "As long as we're at war with England, we will not be able to buy English wool, or fine steel scissors, or even new darning needles."

George had just finished winding some blue yarn into a ball. Now he jumped off his stool, threw the ball at John, and yelled, *"Wham! That's a cannon ball! You're sunk, John! You're sunk! I'm Oliver Perry and you're a British ship, and I sunk you!"*

"Yes, you sunk me, all right!" John laughed as he picked up the ball and wound up the loose end of the yarn. He was thinking that his little brother was pretty smart to have remembered Lieutenant Perry's name. But all the boys talked about the hero of Lake Erie! George had often heard them.

John remembered how he and Seth had stood on the court house steps last September and cheered when the stage brought the news of the victory for the Americans.

"Hooray for Perry!" the boys had shouted, along with the rest of the crowd. Now John thought of something else.

"George, I'll bet you don't know what Perry said when he won that battle!"

"Yes, I do," George insisted. "He said, 'I won! I won!'"

"No, he didn't!" John shook his head. "He said, 'We've met the Enemy and they are ours!'" John said proudly, looking at his mother.

"That's right, John," Mrs. Deere nodded. "Those were Lieutenant Perry's very words." Then she added, "If you're going to polish those needles, you'd better get started. Betsey, it's time to light the sewing dips. Put one on the table by John. He'll need a good light to see by."

Mrs. Deere looked at George. He was getting ready to throw the yarn ball at John again. His eyes were full of mischief.

"George, put that down," she said firmly. "I think you need some exercise, young man! Put on your coat and cap. You may fill the woodbox before it's too dark."

George ran happily into the kitchen. He felt important. Carrying in wood from the woodpile was usually John's work.

For an hour John polished needles. He liked to see them shine like silver in the candlelight. One big darning needle had a deep rust spot. He kept pushing the needle in and out of the strawberry, but the spot wouldn't come off. He was still working on it when his mother called him to supper. He didn't want to give up until he had made the needle shine.

"There's a rusty place on this darning needle that I can't get off," he said disgustedly.

"Well, I'm sure you've done the best you could, John," his mother comforted him.

All through supper John thought about that needle. Surely it could be polished. He needed something harder than the emery powder in the strawberry. Suddenly he had an idea.

"The whetstone!" he said excitedly. "Where's our whetstone?" Everyone stared at him.

"You'd better stick to the baked beans, John," Francis said jokingly. "A whetstone would be rather hard to chew!"

Everyone laughed. John didn't think it was funny. "I need the whetstone to polish that old darning needle," he explained seriously. "I think I can make the needle smooth."

"The whetstone is on top of the cupboard," Mrs. Deere said. "You may get it after you've finished eating."

John finished quickly. He excused himself
from the table, got the whetstone, and took it
into the sewing room. He rubbed the needle
back and forth on the stone. Soon the rust was
gone. Then he polished it with the strawberry.

Finally it was as smooth as the rest of the needles. Most problems could be solved, he decided, if people would only think.

John ran back into the kitchen. "Look, Mother," he cried. "This was the rusty needle. Now it's just as shiny as the others!"

Mrs. Deere took the needle and rolled it between her fingers. "Why, so it is, John! You did a fine job!"

She smiled across the table at the other children and said, "You know, John has just proved the truth in a poem I once learned."

"Say it for us, Mother!" Betsey urged.

"Well, it goes like this——

> If a task is once begun,
> Never leave it till it's done.
> Be the labor great or small
> Do it well—or not at all!"

"Yes, John finished his task and finished it well," Francis agreed. Before he could say more

70

there was a loud knock. George ran to open the door. Mr. Miller, Seth's father, was standing there. He stomped the snow from his boots and stepped inside.

"Good evening, everyone!" he said, taking off his tall hat. "Mrs. Deere, my wife asked me to stop and see if her cape and hood were finished."

"Yes, they are, Mr. Miller," Sarah Deere replied. "Come over by the fire and warm yourself while I get them for you."

Their visitor warmed his hands in front of the fireplace. "I'll wager you young ones are glad tomorrow's Saturday!" he said.

"It's a special Saturday, too," William explained. "It's John's birthday."

"That's right, Mr. Miller. I'll be ten years old tomorrow—February 7," John said proudly, standing straight and tall.

"Well now, that makes the second reason

for my stopping here even better!" Mr. Miller grinned at John. "How would you like a birthday trip in my sleigh?"

"A trip!" everyone cried.

"In a sleigh? With bells on the horses? I want to go too!" George was jumping up and down. "May I go too?"

John was so surprised he couldn't speak. He seldom had a chance to take a trip.

Mr. Miller looked over at the children's mother and explained, "I have to take my wife to Vergennes tomorrow. Her sister is very ill. Seth wanted John to go with us if he could. We'll stay over Sunday at Grandma Martin's and drive back Monday."

John held his breath while he waited to hear his mother's answer. Vergennes was a town fifteen miles north of Middlebury. Fifteen miles was a long way to go in a sleigh!

"Well, that's very kind of you, Mr. Miller,"

his mother said slowly, "but John would have to miss school——"

"I'll bring his lessons home, Mother," Betsey offered quickly.

"What do you think, Francis?" Sarah Deere asked her oldest son.

"At Vergennes they will see Lieutenant MacDonough building his ships. I hear that's quite a sight, Mother! John would never forget it." Francis sounded excited, too.

Mrs. Deere saw the whetstone John still held in his hand. It reminded her of how well John always did his tasks. "Tomorrow is his birthday," she said aloud. "Yes, John, you may go, but you'll have to do your lessons when you get home."

"Oh, I will, Mother, I will!" he promised eagerly. "I'll do all my lessons."

"I want to go, too! I want to go, too!" George begged. "I want to see the ships!"

73

Mr. Miller laughed and rumpled George's hair. "I'm afraid you're a bit too young." He put on his hat and turned to John. "Wear your warmest clothes, boy. It will be a long, cold ride. We'll stop for you at seven o'clock tomorrow morning."

"I'll be ready," John answered. He opened the door for Seth's father. "Good-by and thank you!" he called.

After he closed the door he ran to his mother and hugged her. "I'm going to Vergennes in a sleigh!" he cried. "On my tenth birthday, too! What a birthday present!"

A Birthday to Remember

It was fun riding behind Mr. and Mrs. Miller in the back seat of the sleigh. The runners slid fast over the hard-packed snow. The bells on the horses' harness jingled merrily in the crisp morning air. Both boys felt that such a long journey was a real adventure.

Seth and John were warm under their buffalo robe. Early that morning Mrs. Miller had heated bricks in her oven. The boys rested their feet, clad in heavy boots, on these bricks.

John had already received his birthday present, a new red muffler, from his mother and sister. Betsey had been proud that she had

75

helped knit it. The muffler was now tied around John's heavy collar.

When the horses climbed a small hill, they bobbed their heads and snorted. Their breath looked like puffs of smoke.

John pointed toward the snow-covered mountains to the east. "The Green Mountains aren't very green now," he said.

"No," Seth answered, "but there's a lot of green pines under that snow."

Before long Mr. Miller guided the horses through a covered bridge. As they came out the other side, three deer jumped across the road in front of the sleigh and bounded off into the woods.

"Think we'll see any wolves?" John asked a bit fearfully. Every winter the boys heard stories about wolves that got so hungry they followed people in sleds or sleighs.

"Golly, I hope so!" Seth replied bravely.

76

"Papa brought his gun along. I'd sure like to see him shoot some old wolves."

John wondered if Mr. Miller was a good shot. It would be exciting to have wolves chasing after the sleigh. But the horses might get scared and run. The sleigh might even turn over!

"Will we see any wolves, Papa?" Seth called above the jingle of the bells.

"No, son, not likely," his father answered, glancing back. "Not in the daytime. Besides, we're not carrying fresh meat. That's what wolves like."

John felt better. He didn't really want to see any wolves!

"Look up ahead, John!" Seth shouted. "See what we're going to pass!"

Mr. Miller swung the horses into the deeper snow to pass a long sled pulled by four oxen. The sled was piled high with logs.

"Hello! Hello!" the boys yelled and waved to the driver.

"I reckon that timber is going to Vergennes, too," Mr. Miller shouted. "MacDonough's ships take a lot of lumber!"

John looked off across the snow-covered valley to the west. He couldn't see Lake Champlain, but he knew it was over there— maybe ten or fifteen miles away. The lake was frozen over now, so there wouldn't be any boats on it. But next summer——

"Mr. Miller," he said, leaning forward. "Do you think Lieutenant MacDonough's ships will be ready to fight the English on Lake Champlain next summer?"

"I don't doubt it, lad!" Seth father called back. "I look for a mighty big battle when MacDonough's fleet meets the British!"

"Who do you think will win that battle, Papa?" Seth shouted.

"Why, MacDonough, son! He's out to scuttle the English for sinking his sloops and capturing his crews last summer!"

"Better not talk so loud in this cold air," Mrs. Miller warned. "You'll all make your throats sore."

As the Millers' sleigh approached Vergennes, it passed many more sleds. Some carried logs. Others were loaded with tubs of lard and wooden pails of honey or maple syrup. Some were hauling sacks of grain. There were many men and horses to feed in Vergennes.

John and Seth were feeling cramped and cold when the horses finally pulled the sleigh up the hill and into the main street of the town. The boys saw more oxcarts, sleds, and men on horseback than they had ever seen before. Vergennes was a busy place.

Right on the corner was the tall stone building where Lieutenant MacDonough had his headquarters. At the side of the building men were using a rope and pulley to lift big wooden boxes to the second floor, and from there into the warehouse.

Mr. Miller had to stop his team while a big sled pulled by eight oxen creaked past. The sled was filled with red-colored dirt.

"What's that, Papa?" Seth asked.

"That's iron ore, boys," explained Mr. Miller. "The men down at the blast furnace will melt it into bars. Then they'll send it over to the rolling mill where it will be pressed out into sheets and rods. MacDonough needs a lot of iron as well as wood!"

Mr. Miller drove out to the edge of town where Seth's Aunt Hetty lived. It was Aunt Hetty who was ill. Mrs. Miller took the bag of medicines and herbs she had brought from Middlebury and went in to see her sister.

Seth's father turned the sleigh around and

drove back to Grandma Martin's big white house. The boys were glad to get out and stretch their legs. Then they hurried into the warm kitchen that smelled of Saturday's baking. Suddenly they realized how hungry they were.

"Here's some hot potato soup and bread just out of the oven," Grandma Martin said as she put three bowlsful on the table and cut a warm loaf of bread.

"This is the very best bread I ever ate!" John complimented Seth's grandmother.

"Well, boys," Mr. Miller said after they had eaten and were warm again. "Shall we walk down below the falls and see the ships that are being built there?"

"Yes, let's go!" John said eagerly as Seth ran to get their coats.

The waterfall had frozen into wide sheets of ice with jagged edges and huge icicles. But the boys hardly noticed the waterfall. They had stopped to stare at the scene along the shore of the basin below the falls.

On the edge of ice-covered Otter Creek the framework of three huge ships rose almost as high as Grandma Martin's house. Men seemed to be everywhere. The air was filled with the sounds of sawing, hammering, and shouting.

Between the big hulls of the ships were many new log shops with big brick or stone chimneys. The blacksmiths worked in these shops. The *clang* of heavy sledge hammers pounding on iron split the air.

The three visitors made their way between the wagons and piles of lumber to where they could look inside one of the blacksmith shops. A fire burned bright and hot in the forge.

Whang! Clang! The smith was bending a red-hot sheet of iron over the horn, or pointed end of his anvil. Sparks flew against his leather apron. Sweat glistened on his forehead.

A boy of about sixteen was heating an iron rod in the center of the forge. Now and then he pumped the handle of the bellows to make the fire burn hotter.

"Striker!" shouted the blacksmith.

The boy left the forge, picked up a large hammer, and stood waiting beside the anvil.

With a pair of tongs the blacksmith took a hot, pointed chisel from the forge. He placed the chisel over a mark on the sheet of iron. "Strike!" he called.

Down came the boy's big hammer. The chisel made a hole in the metal plate. The blacksmith moved the chisel to another mark.

"Strike!" he said again. Down came the hammer and another hole was made.

John was fascinated and watched the work closely. He wished he could be a "striker."

Suddenly there was a loud shout from behind them. "Look out below!"

Mr. Miller, Seth, and John turned just in time to see something plunge down from the hull of the nearest ship.

A man passing by with a plank over his shoulder gave a cry and fell to the ground. Mr. Miller and the boys ran over to him.

"My leg! My leg!" he moaned. Blood was spurting from a jagged cut above his knee. The smith, his helper, and other workmen came running. Soon a crowd had gathered.

"Stand back!" the blacksmith commanded. With his powerful hands he ripped the stout trouser cloth away from the deep wound.

"It looks as if that cut goes clear to the bone," Mr. Miller said. "We need something to tie around the leg to stop the bleeding."

He looked up hopefully at the circle of workers. One man started to take off his heavy wool shirt.

John put his hand up to his new muffler. It

was his mother's birthday present to him, but this man needed it worse than he did. Without hesitating he jerked off the long red wrapper and handed it to Mr. Miller.

Soon Mr. Miller had tied the muffler above the cut. The bleeding stopped. The smith and Seth's father lifted the injured man and carried him over to a wagon.

John bent over and picked up a long, sharp spike. "This must be what came flying through the air and hit him," he said.

"Let's see that, son." A man in an officer's uniform stepped forward and held out his hand. "Yes, it has blood on it. My men are working hard, and sometimes they hurry so fast that they're careless."

"Are you Lieutenant MacDonough?" Seth asked the tall, handsome young officer.

"That I am, lad," the officer replied, placing his hand on John's shoulder.

"I saw you give away your fine muffler," he continued. "We'll certainly whip the enemy when even our boys are willing to give up something for their country."

The Lieutenant started toward the wagon. Then he stopped and looked back. "What's your name, boy?" he asked.

"John. John Deere," came the answer. Somehow John had never felt so proud of his name as he did at that time.

Hammer and Knife

It was a Saturday in April. The sun was warm and the sky was blue. Green leaves tinted the woods along Otter Creek.

John was walking down the road carrying his boots. He liked to feel the cool mud squish up between his toes. It was good to go barefoot again. It was good to feel the warmth of spring after the long cold winter.

"Wait up, John! Wait up!"

John turned and saw Peter Goodrich hurrying to catch up with him. Peter couldn't run very fast because his boots sank up to his ankles in mud at every step.

"Hey, did your mother say you could go bare-foot?" Peter yelled.

"Nope." John shook his head. "But it's not cold. I don't reckon she'll care."

"I bet she will!" Peter declared as he reached John. "My mother said I'd get a lickin' if I did. She said I'd get sick like Seth."

Seth hadn't been to school for two weeks. He had been very ill.

"Seth is lots better," John was glad to tell Peter. "But he can't come outdoors yet. He has to stay inside and take old cough sirup."

Peter looked longingly at John's muddy bare feet. Then he thought of the bitter cough medicine on the kitchen shelf at home. He decided to mind his mother.

"I saw you take a big package to Mrs. Dickinson, John," he said as they splashed along. "My mother said I could go with you if you have anything else to deliver."

"No, I don't have any more errands to do this morning," John replied. "I'm going down to Captain Lawrence's. I saw Mr. Storrs turn down there a bit ago with his ox team."

"You think maybe he's going to have them shod?" Peter asked hopefully. It was always fun to watch the blacksmith work. The boys especially liked to be at the shop when he was putting new shoes on oxen.

"Yep, I got a notion he is," John answered. "Come on. Let's hurry."

The boys turned off the muddy street into a side road. They followed the road down a steep hill toward Otter Creek. The blacksmith shop was near the bottom of the hill.

Sure enough, Captain Lawrence was just prodding one of Mr. Storrs' red oxen up the sloping ramp into the ox frame. The ox frame looked a little like a horse stall. It stood on a level place on one side of the shop.

90

"Gid-up there, Goliath!" The smith whacked the ox on its broad flank. Slowly Goliath lumbered up into the stall.

The boys stood out of the way and watched the smith pull a wide leather belt under the animal's belly. He fastened the belt to a short chain. The chain was attached to a big wooden roller in the frame above.

"Moo-oo!" bellowed Goliath. He didn't like to be in this strange stall.

Captain Lawrence turned the handle on the roller. As the roller went around, it wound up the chain. The leather belt under the ox tightened. The muscles in the smith's arm bulged as he turned the handle some more. The belt lifted Goliath right off his feet.

"Moo-oo! Moo!" the ox bellowed again. He didn't like standing on air!

"Is that the only way you can shoe an ox, Captain Lawrence?" John asked.

"Why, hello there, boys!" the smith greeted them as he came around behind the frame. "It's the best way, John," he explained. "Most oxen are too heavy to stand on three legs. Knew a fellow once who tried to shoe one without a frame. Ox fell on him. Broke his leg and the ox's leg, too!"

"Golly, I wouldn't want a big old ox to fall on me!" Peter exclaimed.

The boys watched while the smith lifted Goliath's hind legs and strapped them to flat iron bars on each side of the ramp.

"There now, big fellow," he told the ox, "if you just don't switch me with that muddy tail, I'll have some new hardware on those hooves in just a jiffy."

Peter and John went inside the shop with Captain Lawrence. As the smith took two small curved pieces of iron from a box, he glanced over at John.

"Better put on those boots, boy," he advised. "Wouldn't want you to step on a nail or a piece of hot iron!"

He looked at John again. "Seems as if you get bigger and taller every time I lay eyes on you! Keep on a-growing like that, John, and I'll have to make a striker out of you!"

John grinned happily as he pulled on his boots. That would be fine with him! He remembered the striker he had seen working in Vergennes. When he had his boots on, he stepped over to the row of hammers along the workbench. He picked up a medium-sized hammer and lifted it above his head.

"I could strike a blow with this one right now," he declared.

"Well, now, I believe you could," the smith agreed. "Peter, you pump those bellows, and we'll soon see if John can help me make this shoe for Goliath."

In a few minutes Captain Lawrence had the hot, moon-shaped piece of iron on the anvil. With a pair of tongs he held a flat-headed punch on it.

"Don't think we'll need that big hammer, John," he said. "Take this smaller one and when I say 'Strike,' bring it down square on the punch. Not too hard, mind!"

John took the smaller hammer and stood beside the blacksmith. He felt very grown-up!

"Strike!"

Down came John's hammer. His aim was true. A neat square nail hole was made in the shoe. Captain Lawrence moved the punch to the next mark, and John got ready.

"Strike!"

Another hole was made. John loved the ringing sound of the hammer hitting the metal.

"That doesn't look much like a horseshoe," Peter remarked.

"You're right, lad," the smith agreed. "An ox has to have a shoe made in two parts because his hoof is divided. "We'll have to make four pieces for Goliath's two shoes."

When they had punched all the nail holes, he patted his striker on the back.

"You never missed a blow!" Captain Lawrence said admiringly. "Think you'd like to be a blacksmith some day?"

"I sure would!" John exclaimed. His blue eyes sparkled with pleasure. "I'd rather be a blacksmith than anything else!"

"Well, when Mr. Storrs comes for Goliath, I'll tell him his ox was shod by John Deere!" The smith chuckled as he added, "Maybe I shouldn't, though. What if old Goliath takes off down the road as fast as a deer?"

The boys laughed. It was funny to imagine slow, plodding Goliath bounding down the road because he had on Deere shoes!

As the boys came out of the shop, John looked over at Otter Creek. Along its banks the willows waved their new green leaves in the sun. Suddenly he had an idea.

"Let's get some willow branches over there and make whistles, Peter," he suggested.

"I don't know how," Peter replied. "Besides, I haven't got a knife!"

"I'll show you how," John offered. "We can take turns using this knife."

He took an old folding knife out of his pocket.

"My brother Francis gave it to me because it was so nicked-up and rusty. But I used a whetstone on it and polished and polished. Just feel how sharp it is now!"

Peter carefully touched the blade. "Golly, it sure is sharp. Let's go make the whistles! Just show me what to do."

Down at the edge of the Creek, John cut off a willow branch about one-half inch thick. From

96

this he cut two pieces. One was about six inches long, and the other was about a foot long. He gave the short one to Peter.

"Why are they different lengths?" Peter wanted to know. "Why is yours so much longer?"

"Because I'm going to try something new," John replied as he slanted both ends to flat points. "I've heard about double whistles, but I've never seen one. I'm going to see if I can make a whistle at each end. You watch me and do just what I do."

John handed the knife to Peter. "Be sure to cut away from yourself!" he warned.

After Peter had slanted the end of his stick, John showed him how to clip off the tip of the point. Next, he made a V-shaped notch about one-half inch back from each of his two points. Then Peter cut his notch.

"Now comes the hard part," John told him. "We've got to slip the bark off our whistles. The

bark mustn't split, or we'll have to get new branches and start all over."

Carefully John made a cut all the way around the willow, about three inches back of the notch. He did this on both ends. Then, with the handle of the knife he gently tapped the bark all around the whistle.

"Why are you tapping it?" asked Peter.

"To loosen the bark from the wood," John explained. "Now it will slip off easier."

When he had the bark off both ends of his whistle, he watched while Peter did the same. The wood was white and slippery.

"Now we have to carve off some of the wood back of the notch," John directed, "and a little bit in front of the notch."

Peter watched closely. "You're cutting that end deeper than the other!" he warned.

"I meant to," John answered. "Now this end will have a lower sound—I think."

After Peter had carved his whistle, he asked, "Are we ready to put the bark back on our whistles now?"

"First we'd better go soak them in the creek," John decided. "If the wood's wet, the bark will slide on easier."

Soon the whistles were ready to blow.

"Whee-ee-ee!" Peter's made a high sound.

"Whee-ee-ee! Whee-ee-ee!" One end of John's made a high sound, too.

"Now blow the other end!" Peter said delightedly. "See if the sound is different."

"Whoo-oo-oo!" whistled the deeper cut.

"Whee-ee-ee, whoo-oo-oo, whoo-oo-oo, whee-ee!" John switched from one end to the other as quickly as he could.

"You did it, John!" Peter was happy for his friend. "You made two sounds!"

"Whee! Whee! Whee!" Peter blew three short blasts on his whistle. "But I like my little

100

whistle best, 'cause I made it myself," he said, looking at it proudly.

John was carving something in the middle of his long whistle. When he finished, he showed it to Peter.

"S.M." Peter read. "What's that mean?"

"That's for Seth Miller," John explained. "I'm going to take this whistle to Seth."

"You're going to give it away?" Peter could hardly believe it.

"Yep, I sure am," John nodded. "Seth will like it. Besides, I can always make another one." He thought a moment. "Wonder if I could put two notches in each end? Next time I'll bet I can make an even better whistle."

A Poisonous Plow

THAT SUMMER JOHN and his friends often played down by the creek near the blacksmith shop. One afternoon he and Seth carved wooden boats and sailed them in the shallow water.

"This is MacDonough's big 'Saratoga'!" John cried as he pushed his boat away from the bank with a stick. That was the name of the Lieutenant's largest ship—the one from which the spike had fallen and hurt the man's leg.

"Mine is the British 'Confiance'! Watch out! I'm going to ram you!" Seth yelled.

"Bang! Bang!" John shouted, turning his boat away from Seth's. "I hit you broadside!"

"No, you didn't! You missed! Besides I don't see any guns on your boat!"

"Maybe you can't see them, but Francis told me the 'Saratoga' has twenty-six guns! It took eighty ox teams to haul them over the snow from Troy, New York!"

"I wish we could really put guns on our boats," Seth said, picking his "Confiance" out of the water and looking it over.

John pushed the "Saratoga" over to the bank. "Let's go ask Captain Lawrence for some bent horseshoe nails," he suggested. "He'll be glad to let us have 'em. We can straighten them out and nail them into the sides for guns. Come on, let's put on the guns and then come back!"

The boys took their boats and ran up the path to the shop. Three wagons were pulled up in front of the building. Captain Lawrence stood in the doorway. He was talking to two farmers, Mr. Mattocks and Mr. MacDonald.

John and Seth knew better than to interrupt. They leaned against the ox frame and watched another man lift a wooden plough from the back of his wagon. They recognized Mr. Seth Storrs, the man who owned Goliath.

Mr. Storrs set his plow down near the door of the shop and spoke to the smith. "Would you have time to fix my plow today, Captain? Broke that iron point again on a rock!"

"You mean you've got rocks in your field?" Samuel Mattocks pretended to be shocked. Captain Lawrence and Mr. MacDonald laughed. The boys chuckled. It was a joke because all New England farmers had rocky fields.

"Not rocks," Mr. Storrs joked back. "I just got one rock. But that one jumped right out of the ground and broke my plow!" Then he said seriously, "Well, I've got fewer than last year, anyway. My young ones have had Goliath hitched to the stone boat most of the summer.

I'll wager those boys have a pile of rocks now 'most as high as this blacksmith shop!"

John and Seth looked at each other and grinned. Sometimes they were glad they lived in town. They had heard the farm boys tell what hard work it was to harvest rocks! First they had to go out in the fields and fill the low, heavy box, or stone boat, with rocks. Then the ox pulled the stone boat to the edge of the field. There the boys had to toss the rocks onto a pile. No matter how many trips they made, they could never seem to get all the rocks! More rocks seemed to come from the ground.

"I get tired of just clearing the rocks out of our garden!" Seth said to John.

Mr. Storrs noticed the boys. "Why, there's the lad who made those Deere shoes for Goliath!" he exclaimed.

John smiled but he felt embarrassed. He knew he hadn't really made the shoes.

"Reckon that's how come Goliath could move that stone boat so fast!" Mr. Storrs told the men. Then he winked at them and asked the boys, "How'd you fellows like to come out to my place and help old Goliath harvest rocks?"

Seth shook his head, but John looked at the broken piece of metal and answered, "I'd a lot rather help fix your plow, Mr. Storrs!"

"Oh, you would? Well, tell you what, John," Mr. Storrs continued to tease, "Instead of just fixing this one, why don't you make me a whole new one that won't break on the next rock I hit?" Again the men laughed. John did, too. He was wishing, though, that he could help the blacksmith fix that plough.

Captain Lawrence bent and examined the broken plow. "Wood still seems to be good and solid," he informed Mr. Storrs. "I can bolt on a new iron share, Seth. But I can't promise it won't break again the first time you hit a stone!"

"Did you ever see one of those Newbold plows from New Jersey?" Mr. Storrs asked. "I've heard that only the handles and beam are made of wood. The part that turns the soil is all one piece of cast iron."

"That's right, Seth," answered the smith. "Fellow going through here last fall had one in his wagon. Seemed to me it ought to work a lot better than these wooden ones that just have iron strips bolted on them."

"No, sir!" exclaimed Joseph MacDonald, shaking his head. "You couldn't sell me one of those cast iron plows! Wouldn't risk it! I've heard they poison the soil."

"Well, I don't know about that," Samuel Mattocks spoke up. "But I had a letter last winter from a cousin of mine in New Jersey. He said a farmer near him had bought a Newbold plow. Worked all right, but it made the weeds grow twice as fast as they did before!"

"That's right. That's what I heard, too." Mr. MacDonald nodded. "All that heavy iron turning the ground over poisons the earth and fertilizes the weeds. It's hard enough already to get a decent crop around here."

Mr. Storrs scratched his head thoughtfully. "Poisons the soil and makes the weeds grow, does it?" he repeated. Then he added firmly, "Well, all the same, if I could get a cast iron plow, I'd try it! I'm plumb tired of having the bolts and point break on this wooden one! Just when I need it the most, too!"

A little while later as John and Seth were pounding nails into their boats, John said, "I think Mr. Storrs was right."

"Right about what?" Seth wanted to know. He had forgotten all about the men and their talk. He was thinking only about the boats.

But John was still thinking about the plough. "I think Mr. Storrs would be right to try a cast iron plough. Iron comes from the soil. I don't see how iron could poison the ground or make weeds grow."

"I'll bet it could! You don't know anything about it!" Seth argued.

"Well, I know iron is just red dirt! Don't you remember that load of iron ore we saw in Vergennes last winter?"

"Sure! It looked like a big load of poison, too!" Seth pounded his last nail.

"If iron poisons the soil, then why don't the beans and potatoes in the garden die? We sure have to hoe them enough with iron hoes!"

"That's it! That's why we have to hoe so often! Those iron hoes make the weeds grow! That's what the men said!" Seth was sure he had won the argument.

John looked thoughtfully at his friend. Maybe Seth was right. Weeds seemed to grow mighty fast in gardens! Could it possibly be because of the iron hoes?

"I'm going to tell papa about iron making weeds grow," Seth declared. "Maybe he won't make me hoe the potatoes." Hoeing potatoes was almost as bad as picking potato bugs!

"You'd better not do that," John warned. "You'd just have to pull weeds by hand!"

Seth looked disappointed. "I guess you're right," he admitted. He had been pleased with his idea. He didn't like garden work.

"What about iron spades and shovels? They don't poison the ground!" John insisted. He thought of something else. "Even the wooden plows have iron on the bottoms."

"Aw, who cares about old plows and iron anyway!" Seth was tired of talking about it. He picked up his boat. "Let's have a battle and see who gets sunk first!"

"All right," John agreed. "My 'Saratoga' has all her twenty-six guns now." As he leaned over to put his boat in the water, he couldn't help saying, more to himself than Seth, "But when I get to be a blacksmith, I'm going to make a cast iron plow, just to prove that it won't poison the soil or make weeds grow!"

The Sounds
of War

"Listen! What's that sound?" Peter Goodrich asked. It was the first week in September. Willie Baker, Peter, John, and Seth were walking home from school. They had just reached the corner by the Meeting House.

"Listen!" Peter said again. "Don't you hear something?"

The boys stopped and listened. From far away came a rolling sound.

"I hear it!" Willie said.

The boys listened again. The sound was a little louder than before.

"It's a drum!" Seth yelled.

Then a man by the courthouse stepped into the street, pointed down the road, and shouted, "Here comes a company of Volunteers!"

The boys ran across the street, through the park, and over to the courthouse. The sound of the drum was plainer now. People were hurrying out of stores along Merchants' Row.

"It must be the Bethel Company! The stage driver said they were coming this way!" one man called excitedly.

"I heard they made Charter Dunham their Captain," another man answered.

When, far down the street, the boys could see the marching men, they ran to meet them.

"Ker-rump! Ker-rump! Ker-rumpity-rumpity-rump!" beat the drum. The men marched in step. They carried muskets over their shoulders.

"Hooray for the United States! Hooray for Vermont!" yelled the boys as they ran along beside the soldiers!

"Hooray for the Green Mountain Boys!" shouted old Mr. Davis, throwing his hat in the air. Many years ago he had fought in the War for Independence. Then the Vermont soldiers had been called the Green Mountain Boys.

When the Bethel Company reached the Court House Park, their captain shouted, "Company —Halt! Fall out!"

The men were glad to stop marching and rest under the trees in the park. Many of them gathered at the town pump. They were thirsty, too. It had been a long march from Bethel over Middlebury Mountain.

John and Seth moved closer to a group of soldiers who were sitting on the grass. One of the men looked up and said, "Hello, boys. Want to join the Bethel Company?" Then he saw their slates and school books. "Think your schoolmaster would care if you went off with us to fight the British?"

114

"He might not care, but our mothers certainly would!" Seth answered.

"Do you think there really is going to be a big battle?" asked John.

"Reckon so. But it won't last long if all the officers are as spunky as our Captain Dunham!" the soldier replied proudly.

"That's right," another one agreed. "Tell them what happened at the tollgate, Jeb."

"Well, on the road over the mountain we came to the tollgate," Jeb began. "Captain Dunham says to the tollkeeper, 'We're the Bethel Company. Unlock the gate and let us through.' The gatekeeper shook his head. 'Pay toll for your men first,' he said. That made the captain angry. 'Keeper,' he said, 'we're on our way to fight in the war! Open that gate!'"

Jeb stopped and took a drink of water from a dipper that was handed to him. John and Seth could hardly wait to hear what happened.

"Go on," urged Seth. "What happened? Did the keeper open the gate?"

"He did not!" Jeb declared. "He said, 'I won't unlock this gate until you pay toll!' Well, Captain Dunham's eyes were fairly shootin' sparks, he was so riled! 'We're wanted in Plattsburg, and we're going through!' the Captain shouted to the gatekeeper."

Jeb paused. "What do you think Captain Dunham did then?" he asked the boys.

"I suppose he had the men tear down the gate," John said.

"No," Jeb shook his head. "Captain Dunham aimed his musket at that lock and blew it clear to kingdom-come!"

"Gol-lee! I wish I'd been there!" Seth cried. "I wish I could have seen that."

"Served that tollkeeper right!" John nodded approvingly. "He should have been proud to let you soldiers go through free!" He was remembering that Lieutenant MacDonough had told him it was good to have people give up something to help their country.

The next few days were exciting ones. From all the nearby farms and villages men were leaving their work and joining the Volunteers. Everyone was talking about the big battle that was sure to come soon.

The Volunteers would fight the English army that was coming down from Canada. Lieutenant MacDonough's ships would meet the British fleet on Lake Champlain.

The boys were so excited they could hardly keep their minds on their school lessons. It was their keen interest in the war that got John and Seth in trouble that next Sunday, September 11, 1814.

The morning was sunny and warm. Right after church the two boys met and started home ahead of their families. They had almost reached the bridge when they heard the pounding hoofbeats of a horse coming. In a moment a rider turned into Main Street from the Weybridge road. He galloped over the bridge and past the boys. They turned to watch.

When he reached Merchants' Row, he shouted, "The battle's on! You can hear the cannons loud and clear out at Weybridge!" Then he galloped on to spread the news.

"Did you hear that, Seth?" John was excited. "Lieutenant MacDonough is out on the lake fighting in a battle right now!"

"Gol-lee! I sure wish we could see that battle!" Seth exclaimed.

"So do I," replied John. "But if we can't see it, at least we can hear it—if we go out to Weybridge!"

"Then let's go! Weybridge isn't so far!"

The boys began to run. They dashed across the bridge, ran past John's house, and turned down Weybridge street. Before they had left the town, they were out of breath.

"We can't—run all—the way!" puffed Seth. They slowed down to a walk.

"I should have gone back and asked Mother if I could go," John admitted.

"Oh, we won't be gone long," Seth assured him. But John felt guilty. He knew that Weybridge was several miles away.

"Let's hurry! Let's run!" he said. They ran until they were tired. Then they walked.

Suddenly John stopped. "Wait a minute, Seth. Listen. Can you hear any shooting yet?"

The boys stood very still. They heard a cowbell jingle. They heard the barking of a dog faraway. But they didn't hear any cannons.

"Guess we aren't close enough," John decided. They began to run again.

This time Seth stopped suddenly. "I hear something!" he declared.

John listened. Then he looked back. "You hear that wagon coming?" he asked Seth. "Maybe we can catch a ride."

"It's Mr. Davies!" exclaimed Seth. "That's his team and wagon."

The old man, who had once been a Green Mountain Boy, stopped the horses when he saw the boys. "You lads want a lift?" he asked.

"Yes, thanks!"

John followed Seth up over the dusty wheel and into the back of the wagon. The wheel rubbed against his Sunday pants.

"Guess we should have changed our clothes before we started on this trip," John said.

"If I had gone home first, my mother probably wouldn't have let me come," Seth admitted.

John frowned. He knew they were doing wrong. But they were in the wagon now, and the horses were trotting down the road. Soon they would get to Weybridge and then they could hear the "Saratoga's" big guns. John forgot his worry.

"Whoa! Whoa, there!" Mr. Davis pulled on the reins. The horses stopped. "Listen to that, boys!" he cried. From far away came a low rumble like distant thunder.

"Is that cannon fire?" asked John.

Mr. Davis slapped the reins, and the horses trotted on. "That sure enough is cannon fire! he answered. "What a bloody battle must be going on over there!"

The old gentleman shook his head. "Those cannon balls are wicked cruel. Why, I've seen them take a man's head off clean as a whistle!"

John's eyes opened wide. Seth's fingers tightened on the wagon box.

"Yep," Mr. Davis went on. "You lads can be mighty glad you're not out there fightin'! You'd have smoke and fire all around you! Cannon balls smashing into your ship! You'd hear the screams of the wounded and dying——" He paused, lost in thoughts of the past.

Clearer now came the low rumbling *Ker-Boo-ooM* from the distant guns.

"John," said Seth in a small scared voice, "let's go home."

John nodded. With every *Ker-Boo-ooM* he could picture men being blown apart. The war didn't sound exciting now. It wounded too real, too horrible, and too close!

"Now, I remember one time——" old Mr. Davis began. But the boys didn't hear. They were climbing over the end of the wagon. Together they jumped to the ground. Seth's foot hit a rock and he fell. He cried out.

"Are you hurt?" John inquired anxiously, as he helped Seth to his feet.

"I must have twisted my ankle!" Seth groaned. Carefully he took a step. "I guess I can walk, but it certainly hurts!"

The boys looked down the road. Middlebury seemed to be a long way back. Slowly, with Seth limping painfully, they started toward home. "Someone will come along and give us a ride," John said hopefully.

Seth was fighting to keep the tears back. John felt like crying, too.

"I wish it were my ankle that was hurt, Seth," John told his friend. "I wish I had never thought of going to hear those old cannons!"

Before long Seth's ankle was swollen above his shoe top. The boys were dusty, tired, and miserable when a man in a carriage finally came along and took them the rest of the way home.

Later that day John sat at the kitchen table, writing a sentence which his mother had given him. "Think what it means each time you write it," she had said sternly.

With a goose quill pen he wrote the sentence over and over in his copy book.

124

If we do wrong, we cannot have a joyful heart. If we do wrong, we cannot have a joyful heart.

"A postrider just crossed the bridge!" George shouted from the shop. "Come on! Let's go hear the news about the battle!"

Francis, William, and Betsey hurried out the door. John laid down his pen and looked hopefully at his mother.

Mrs. Deere shook her head. "Write your sentence, John," she said quietly.

John picked up his goose quill pen and wrote the sentence again.

If we do wrong, we cannot have a joyful heart.

It was true. He had done wrong and his heart was certainly heavy! Everyone else would hear details about the battle and know who won before he did—even George! Besides, John wanted to hear the news from the post-rider.

But worse than writing all these sentences was the rule that he couldn't play with Seth for two whole weeks! It seemed to John as if hours went by before George came bursting into the house again shouting the news.

"MacDonough beat the British!"

"Hooray!" cried John, starting up from his chair. Then he sat down again. "Was Lieutenant MacDonough hurt?" He asked his little brother anxiously.

"No, but another man's head came sailing through the air and knocked him down!"

"George!" Mrs. Deere was shocked.

"I heard the postrider tell about it, I did!" George insisted.

"I'm glad Francis wasn't old enough to volunteer!" John said thankfully. "This morning I thought it would be exciting to see a battle— or even hear one. But I didn't like the sound of the cannons!" He looked up at his mother and asked, "Did a lot of men really die in that battle today, Mother?"

"I'm afraid so, son," she answered sadly.

"From now on," John said seriously, "I hope the loudest noise I ever hear is Captain Lawrence pounding on his anvil!"

Hard Times, Hard Work

JOHN WATCHED his mother reach to the top shelf of the kitchen cupboard, take down the small tin money box, and open it.

"I wish times weren't so hard," she sighed as she took out a coin.

"I don't think times are as hard as subtraction," said George, who had just finished his third year in school. He frowned as Mrs. Deere and John laughed.

"Mother didn't mean arithmetic," explained John. "She meant hard times. You know, George, when it's hard for people to get money, they say times are hard."

"Then we have hard times all the time, don't we?" George asked.

"It seems that way, George," Mrs. Deere answered. "I thought last year after the war was over, that our tailoring shop would have more customers. But now people just don't have any money to pay for sewing."

"Maybe the farmers will have good crops this year, Mother," John said. He was thinking of last year, the coldest summer people could remember. There had been snow long into the summer months and frosts even in July and August. In the fall there was no harvest, for nothing had grown. Because the farmers had no crops to sell, they had no money to buy things from the stores and shops in town.

The Deeres, like many other families in Middlebury, had to make every penny go as far as possible. In the spring they had moved to a small house near the northeast edge of town.

"The rent is cheaper here, and we can have a big garden," Mrs. Deere had explained.

Now she gave a coin to John. "Please go to Dickinson's store," she said, "and buy a pound of codfish, a small package of tea, and a spool of black thread."

"I wish I could earn some more money," John said wistfully.

"Why, John, you've been a big help!" his mother declared. "That's probably one of the coins you put in the box yourself! For a boy of only twelve, you've earned a lot!"

All winter John had been collecting wood ashes and selling them to Mr. Page, who made potash. It took a long time to collect enough good ashes to earn a coin. But John had worked hard at it. Nearly every week during the winter he had been able to put a coin into their box.

"But now that it's summer, there won't be so many ashes," he replied sadly.

"We still have to burn wood to cook and bake," Mrs. Deere reminded him. Then she thought of some good news. "Our money box may fill up quicker, now that summer clothes are needed. Just yesterday, Mrs. Seymour came in and ordered two silk dresses."

"Oh, that's fine, Mother!" John was pleased. He knew Mrs. Seymour wouldn't ask his mother to accept maple syrup or firewood in exchange for the sewing. Mrs. Seymour would pay with silver dollars. Her husband was a rich man. He was having a big new house built right across the street from the meeting house.

John remembered another cash customer. "Do you think Miss Painter will need some summer dresses, too?" he asked. Miss Abby Painter was the daughter of Gamaliel Painter, the most important man in Middlebury.

"Yes, John, Miss Painter will probably be in, too." Mrs. Deere smiled fondly at her son. "Now you and George run along to the store. And, John, stop worrying! Soon Francis and I will have more sewing and tailoring than we can do! You wait and see!"

The boys walked down the dusty road. John looked up at the hot blue sky. "If it doesn't rain soon, we'll have to start carrying pails of water to the garden," he told George.

"Last summer it was too cold, and this summer it's too hot!" George said crossly.

The hot, dry weather continued. Every evening the boys pumped water and carried it in big wooden pails to the garden to water the plants. In spite of all they could do, the beans and peas withered and died.

Everyone was hoping for rain. The farmers' crops were burning in the fields. Pastor Merrill held special meetings in the church to pray for rain. Finally the rains came, but not in time to save the gardens or the crops.

"Yes, times are certainly hard," Captain Lawrence said one October afternoon when John was at the smithy. John liked to stop there after school to watch Captain Lawrence work and often to help him.

During the summer the house on the edge of town had been sold. Now the Deeres lived in a yellow building at the east end of Merchants' Row. John was glad they had moved. He liked being near Otter Creek and the blacksmith shop. Today Captain Lawrence was repairing a log chain for Joseph MacDonald.

"Don't rightly know how we're going to get through this winter," Mr. MacDonald said slowly. He sounded very discouraged. "No harvest to speak of for the last two years! Tell you, Captain, if I could sell my farm, I'd pack my family in the wagon and move West!"

The Captain nodded. "A good many Vermonters are doing just that. But, Joseph, times are bound to get better around here, if you can just stick it out."

John felt sorry for farmers like Mr. Mac-Donald. They worked hard to grow crops in their stony fields. When the weather turned against them, all their work was for nothing. Sometimes their families had hardly enough food to live through the long cold winters. Even when there was a good harvest, they took in very little money for their work.

The next two summers were warm, and there was plenty of rain for the crops. "Times are getting better," everyone said.

"Times may be better, but money is still as scarce as hen's teeth," John said to his brother William. It was a warm April evening and the boys were walking over to Seth's house where the singing school was held.

"I'm beginning to wish the hens themselves were scarce, too!" chuckled William.

John smiled. He knew what William meant. Just before they left home, a farmer's wife had brought their mother four dozen eggs and three chickens in payment for some sewing.

"That makes nine dozen eggs we have now!" John exclaimed.

"Tomorrow I'll have to go to the store and see if Mr. Dickinson will trade some salt and tea for eggs," William said.

John looked down at his old shoes. Even though he had used boot black and lard on them, they still looked shabby. He tried to pull his coat sleeves down on his wrists, but the sleeves were just too short for his long arms.

William looked at his brother carefully. "John, that old suit of mine is just too small for you," he stated. "You're taller and more broad shouldered than I was at fifteen!"

"Yes," John agreed, "this suit is too short and too tight. I'm afraid to bend over!"

"Maybe Francis and Mother should make you a new one," William suggested.

"No," John said firmly. "They work too long by candle light as it is. Besides, wool cloth costs too much. If I could just earn some extra money this summer, I'd buy a blue suit and a pair of black shoes I saw at Hagar's store. Don't say anything to Mother about it. If I can, I'm going to surprise her."

Singing school was almost like a party. The young ladies wore their prettiest dresses. The young men wore starched shirts and sat tall and straight before the singing master.

When the singing was over, Mrs. Miller passed a plate of maple sugar candy. John saw Peter Goodrich laughing and talking to the prettiest girl in their class. Peter was wearing a new suit. John felt as if his coat sleeves and pant legs were getting shorter every minute. He stood back out of the candle light.

136

Seth came over and stood beside him. "Wish we had our old clothes on and could go out in the barn and wrestle," he said in a low voice. "Who wants to stand around talking to girls anyway? Who cares about girls?"

"I guess Pete does," John remarked. Then he thought of his problem. "Seth, have you heard of anyone wanting some work done?"

"Papa just said at supper that Mr. Atwood needs someone to turn the grinder at his tannery. I wanted to try it, but Mother said my arms aren't strong enough."

"Do you think I could get the job?" John asked quickly. "I could do it."

"Why sure you could! You can beat all the rest of us at wrestling. I'll bet you could turn that old grinder all day!" Seth was still John's best friend and admirer.

Mr. Atwood was glad to hire such a strong boy. John didn't have to turn the grinder all day—just for a couple of hours each day. But it was hard work grinding oak and hemlock bark. At first his arms ached at night. But in a few days his muscles grew used to the heavy work and he did not mind it.

"You're the best grinder I ever had," Mr. Atwood complimented him. "You can turn that crank faster and longer than most men."

John, with William's help, was able to keep his secret from the rest of the family. By the end of the summer he had saved enough money to buy the blue suit and black shoes.

One Sunday morning he was the last one down to breakfast. He had dressed carefully.

"Why, John Deere!" his mother cried when she saw him. "Where did you ever——" But she was too surprised to finish.

"You look as important as Mr. Painter!" declared George proudly.

"And a lot more handsome!" added Betsey.

138

"How in the world did you manage to buy this suit?" Francis asked, feeling of the fine wool cloth. "You made a fine choice."

"I've been grinding bark for Mr. Atwood," John explained. "This suit probably isn't as well made as you and Mother could have done, but I wanted to save you the work. I wanted to earn it myself and surprise you."

"Well, you most certainly did!" Mrs. Deere exclaimed. "It's a fine suit, John, and it fits you well. I know you needed it and the new shoes, too. We're mighty proud of you!"

William winked at Francis. "Now John won't have to stand back in the corner at singing school. Maybe he'll even be brave enough to talk to some of the girls!"

John grinned and looked down at his shiny shoes. Then he said happily, "If I can keep on grinding bark after school this winter, I'll buy Mother an India silk shawl."

A Better Handle

SARAH DEERE sat at her work table in the tailoring shop. For once her hands were not busy with a needle and thread. She sat quietly reading over an old letter. She was waiting for John to come in and say good-by to her.

Soon she heard him coming down the stairs. She smiled at the heavy, fast footsteps. They were heavy because John was a tall, strong young man of seventeen. They were fast because he was anxious to start his new job.

John put the bundles and clothes he was carrying on a chair. For the next four years he would be living in the Lawrence home at the

140

top of the hill above the blacksmith shop. John knew his leaving made his mother sad, so he tried to cheer her up.

"At last I'm really going to be a blacksmith!" he said joyfully, as he put his arm around his mother's shoulders.

"I'm happy for you, son," she replied, reaching up and patting his hand. "I know it's what you've always wanted, and I'm sure you'll be an excellent smith. Captain Lawrence is one of the best and he will teach you all he knows."

Mrs. Deere pointed to a chair. "Sit down a moment before you go, John. When William became an apprentice, your father wrote this letter to him, and I'd like to have you read it. It has good advice for you, too."

John sat down and took the letter from his mother. In the years since their father had died, Sarah Deere had often opened the box of old letters and read them to the children.

John remembered hearing his mother read this one. But now his father's words seemed to have been meant for him instead of William.

" 'Be faithful to your master and to his interest,' " John read aloud. " 'Be obedient to him; be friendly and kind to all his family. Let truth and honesty be your guide.' "

John looked up at his mother. "I'll remember father's words," he promised. "I'll be a good apprentice to Captain Lawrence."

He was a good apprentice, too. He listened and remembered what the smith told him. He watched carefully. He kept his mind on what he was doing. No matter how small a task he was given, he did it the very best he knew how. John's happiest moments were when the Captain praised him for a job well done.

One day Seth brought in his mother's iron skillet when John was alone in the shop.

"John, this was Mother's favorite spider,"

143

Seth said. "I dropped it on the stone steps and broke off the handle. Do you think you can put the handle back on?"

"I'll sure try," John replied. He pumped the bellows until the forge fire burned just right. Then he put the broken side of the skillet, the broken handle, and a pair of tongs into the fire. He covered them with the hot coke.

"I'll work the bellows," Seth offered.

"Thanks, Seth. But don't pump too hard. I've got to heat the iron slowly. Too much air will make flakes or scale on the iron."

John watched the fire closely. When sharp sparks flew out of the fire, he knew that the metal was ready to join, or weld together.

He handed Seth a pair of tongs. "You'll have to hold the skillet steady on the anvil," he informed his friend.

John's hammer rang out loud and clear as he carefully joined the two broken ends.

144

"You know, John, I think grinding all that bark at the tannery must have helped you develop those big arm muscles," Seth reasoned.

"Yes, I guess it did," John agreed. "At least my arms never get tired now, no matter how long I work at the anvil."

Seth looked at the skillet. The handle was all in one piece again. John had heated it once more and was smoothing and shaping it.

"Mother will be glad to have her favorite spider again," Seth grinned. "She claims it fries meat better than any other one, but sometimes she burns her hand on that short handle."

"Would you like a longer handle?" John asked. "I could draw this one out and curve it up so it wouldn't be so close to the fire."

"Gol-lee!" Seth exclaimed. "Can you really do that? If you can make that handle longer, Mother will be so glad that she'll forget I ever broke it!"

John laughed. Seth sounded just as he used to when they played together.

A few days later as John and Captain Lawrence were walking up the hill to supper, the blacksmith remarked, "I saw Mrs. Miller in Dickinson's store this morning. She told me what a good helper I've got. Said you'd fixed her broken spider and made it better than new."

John felt pleased, but he said modestly, "Oh, I only welded the broken handle."

"No, she said you made the handle longer and better shaped. That's a good lesson to remember, lad. Always try to think of how something can be improved."

John nodded his head. Then he chuckled as he told the smith, "You know, Captain, I think I got that idea when I was ten years old. That spring I just couldn't rest until I had finally made a willow whistle that would blow two sounds from the same end."

Fire!

"THAT'S A mighty fine smithy you've got there!"
John gave the last nail another blow with his
hammer. Then he turned to see Lemual Derby,
whose farm was just across the road.

"Hello, Lemual," he greeted his neighbor.
John stepped back to look at his new building.
It was his first blacksmith shop. He had built
it himself, and he was really proud of it.

"I guess it will do," he said modestly. "Now
if the folks here in Leicester Four Corners and
the farmers round-about just have enough
work to keep me busy, I'll be right glad I settled
here."

147

"That's why I came over, John," Lemual explained. "I'd like to be the first one in these parts to have a John Deere hay fork! Could you make me one? My cousin in Vergennes has one you made when you worked up there. He claims it slides in and out of the hay as easy as a hot knife cutting butter!"

John laughed. "Well, I do curve the tines and polish them as bright as I used to shine my mother's needles."

At the thought of his mother, John felt sad. Many changes had come in the eight years since he had finished his apprenticeship. There had been much sickness. Nearly every family had lost loved ones. Both his mother and his brother Francis had died.

Betsey still did dressmaking. William was a schoolmaster. George had married and was now far off at sea with the United States Navy.

John looked down the road. He was remembering how he used to push his mother's needles in and out of the little red strawberry. Suddenly his eyes brightened. He saw his pretty young wife, Demarius, coming up the road. In her arms she carried their year-old son, Francis.

"Lemual, tomorrow I'll build the first fire in my forge," John said. "I promise you'll have your hayfork before nightfall."

Then he hurried to meet his wife, took his husky young son and tossed him playfully in the air. "I wish your Uncle Francis could have lived to see what a strapping big namesake he has!" John told the laughing baby.

"Why, John, the shop is all finished, isn't it?" cried Demarius.

"Yes, and I have my first piece of work—a hayfork for Lemual Derby!"

That summer John was indeed busy. Leicester Four Corners was a little village about twelve miles south of Middlebury. Stagecoaches, farm wagons, and carriages came through the Four Corners on their way to bigger towns.

Farmers soon learned that hoes, rakes, and shovels made by the young smith, John Deere, were far better than any others they had had.

The stagecoach drivers sang his praises all along their routes. "Yes, siree!" one of them told another, "When John Deere puts a new band or bolt on a coach, you can be sure it won't work loose. It's on to stay!"

"That's right," the other driver agreed. "He's the best man to turn a shoe, too. A few weeks ago I thought I'd have to get rid of my favorite mare. She kept going lame, no matter how I doctored her. One day I pulled into Four Corners. Molly had gone lame again. In no time young John Deere made a special built-up shoe for her. Do you know, Molly trotted out of there as spry as a colt! Hasn't been lame since. I wish there was a John Deere at all our stops!"

150

But in spite of John's fine workmanship and his growing business, hard times were just ahead for the Deere family. One cold winter night when the wind was blowing hard, John and Demarius heard a pounding on the door.

It was Lemual Derby. "Hurry, John!" he shouted. "Your shop's ablaze!"

John pulled on his trousers over his nightshirt and ran toward the smithy. He got there just in time to see the flaming roof cave in. No one could even get close to the roaring fire.

He stood barefooted in the snow, watching the shop he had so proudly built burn to the ground. His shoulders drooped with discouragement. He could hardly believe it was gone.

Lemual came over and put his hand on John's shoulder. "I'm right sorry!" he said.

The young blacksmith shook his head slowly. Then he straightened his shoulders, lifted his chin, and replied with determination, "That's all right, Lemual. I can build it again. This time I'll improve it some."

Demarius worried because her husband worked so hard. He worked from dawn until dark. Often he forgot to come home to eat.

Demarius, with little Francis toddling along beside her, would take John a basket of lunch she had packed. As he laid aside his hammer and saw and sat down to eat, Demarius' bright eyes would sparkle with pleasure.

He could not talk with her and play with his son for very long. He was too eager to finish the building so he could work at his trade and earn money for his family.

Soon the new shop was completed. John and Demarius thought life was wonderful again. They rejoiced especially because they now had a sweet baby girl whom they named Jennette.

But their troubles were not over. In a few months misfortune came to them again.

153

When John carefully put out his forge fire and went home for the night, a storm with much thunder and lightning had already begun. As he stood looking out the window at the black clouds, a crash of thunder shook the house. At the same time he saw a big bolt of lightning flash down from the sky and strike his new smithy. The shop burst into flames.

As before, nothing could be done to save it. With a heavy heart John stared down at the smoldering ashes and realized that he would have to build his blacksmith shop for the third time. Demarius felt like crying as she stood beside her husband with her arm through his. She could think of nothing comforting to say.

"The Lord sees fit to test us in many ways," John said softly. "But if the first Vermonters could fight the wolves, Indians, and British, I guess we can fight bad luck."

He put his finger under Demarius' chin and

tilted her head up. "We won't be discouraged," he told her. "Back in school Master Hoyt was always saying, 'If at first you don't succeed, try, try, again.' That's what we'll do."

Demarius blinked back her tears and smiled at her tall, broad-shouldered husband. She was proud of his courage.

Their third shop was welcomed eagerly by the farmers and travelers. Once again Demarius was concerned over the long, hard hours John spent at the anvil. But she was even more concerned at the worried expression she saw so often on his face. One evening as she sat sewing by candlelight, John spoke.

"Today a man named Amos Bosworth came to see me. He wants me to move to Royalton and be his master mechanic. He has a big blacksmith shop in connection with the hotel. Six stages begin and end their runs at his shop. It's a busy place, and the pay is good."

Demarius put down her sewing and looked at her husband. He was frowning thoughtfully. "But, John," she said, "you've worked so terribly hard to get a shop of your own! Surely nothing will happen to this one!"

"It doesn't seem likely," he answered. "But I lost so much in both fires that no matter how long I work each day, I can't seem to get ahead. If I worked for Mr. Bosworth, I wouldn't have to keep buying new supplies. Soon we could pay off all our debts."

Now Demarius understood what had been worrying her husband. "I trust your judgment, John," she replied quietly. "You do as you think best. I'm sure you will do the right thing."

So the young John Deere family moved over the Green Mountains and into the valley of the White River. It was a move that was to change their lives, and the lives of many Eastern farmers who would soon be pioneers of the West.

156

The Call of the West

"You lads pile out of that stage! They'll be bringing the horses around any minute now!" Amos Bosworth shouted at the group of boys playing in and on the stagecoach in front of the hotel. "Get down off that seat, you two! That driver will tan your hides if he catches you fellows on his coach!"

John Deere stood in the doorway of the big shop. He rubbed his hands on his leather apron and smiled at the swarm of youngsters jumping out of and off the stagecoach. It didn't seem very long ago that he and Seth had done the same thing—and been chased off, too.

As the driver stepped out on the hotel porch, the two boys on the driver's seat jumped to the ground and scooted behind a farm wagon. "I'll skin you scallywags alive!" he shouted, shaking his fist at the scattering children.

"A stagecoach attracts boys like honeysuckle does the bees!" Amos said to John.

"Right you are!" John chuckled. "We boys in Middlebury used to play on the coaches every chance we got. Once we released the brake and let one roll down a little hill. My friend, Seth, broke his arm when he jumped off! The stage hit a tree, and it took Captain Lawrence two hours to fix the broken wheel!"

"I'll wager you were right there watching the smith work." Amos declared.

"Yes, I was," John admitted. "I worked the bellows for the Captain. But that didn't save me from being punished when my mother heard what had happened!"

Amos nodded and grinned. "I knew you must have been a blacksmith boy! No one could be as fine a smith as you are now if he hadn't been around a forge fire all his life!"

"Well, thank you, Amos," John answered. "It's true that the ring of a hammer on an anvil has always been music in my ears. Speaking of blacksmithing, there's something that's been bothering me lately."

"What's that, John?"

"Fellow came through here yesterday and showed me some shovels, hoes, and rakes made in one of the new factories. He said they turned out more in a week than I could make in a year."

"I guess it's true, John. New factories are being built all through the East. What did you think of those factory shovels?"

"They looked pretty fancy, but they didn't seem very well-made. Handle wasn't made of oak or hard maple. Looked as it if might snap off

159

first time you tried digging out a boulder. That doesn't seem right to me, Amos."

Again Amos nodded in agreement. "Those factories don't much care how long a shovel or a rake lasts. They're just interested in making a lot of them and selling them cheap."

"If I was running a factory," John declared, "I'd want people to be satisfied with my product. I'd make the best shovels or hoes I could, out of the finest materials I could get, even if it meant making fewer of them!"

"I'm sure you would, my friend!" Amos slapped John on the back. Then he laughed. "Now don't go leaving me to run a shovel factory! Why, since you've been taking care of our stages, we've had fewer breakdowns this whole year than we used to have in a month."

John smiled. He was pleased that Amos Bosworth liked his work. Many travelers stayed over night at the hotel. Often they came in-

to the shop to watch the smith at his forge. Many of them were on their way West.

"That's the place to go," they'd tell John. "Out to Ohio or Indiana, or Illinois! Rich farm land as far as the eye can see! Good black soil that will grow anything! You can leave your stone boat here. There's no rocks to dig out of that prairie ground!"

Often John put new iron on wagon wheels for Vermont farmers who were starting westward. "Yes, John," they'd say. "We hate to leave our old home, but times are too hard here! Some years we can't raise a crop at all."

Often John heard the invitation, "Why don't you pack up your family and go with us? We'll need a good blacksmith in our new town."

John smiled and shook his head. Vermont was his home. He loved the Green Mountains and the villages nestled in their quiet valleys. Demarius would hate to go so far away from her father, mother, brothers, and sisters. Her father, William Lamb, had one of the few really good farms in that part of Vermont.

But in the evenings as John rode about the countryside, he often looked at the gold and purple sunset sky and felt a longing to see those rolling prairies of the West.

One evening as Demarius sat rocking their new little daughter, Ellen Sarah, John said, "I know you're lonely here in the country. Now that we have saved some money, I've been thinking of building my own shop in the village of Hancock. What do you think of the idea?"

"I think it would be fine, John. I'd like having closer neighbors, and I know you'd be happier working your own forge."

John Deere built his new smithy close beside a mountain stream. He built a stone dam across this stream and used the waterpower to turn his grindstone. He was kept very busy.

163

His brightly polished hay forks were in great demand. Farmers liked the way he repaired and sharpened all their tools. He made an iron plow for a young farmer. John smiled when he remembered how farmers used to be afraid that iron would poison the soil.

Although he worked long hours at his forge, very little cash money came in return for his labor. As they had at the tailoring shop, people paid their debts by bringing in their extra corn, potatoes, or maple syrup. But John needed money to buy bars of iron and coal for his forge. He needed money to buy clothes for his family.

Demarius and the children lived in a large, comfortable home just a little way down the road from the smithy. Francis, who was seven years old, now had three little sisters. John's face was often lined with worry these days as he tried to work harder than ever to provide for his wife and children.

164

Demarius understood his worry. "John," she said to him one day, "many people owe you money. They must know we have bills to pay, too. Can't you collect money from any of them?"

"Times are hard for everyone," he replied, shaking his head sadly. "What little money the farmers have, they need to buy salt or shoes or medicine. I can't ask them to give me money if it means some child will have to go without a pair of shoes or without medicine."

Demarius looked fondly at her big husband. He was so kind-hearted! She knew he would always help others. Then she sighed as she thought of the things their own children needed.

One evening Demarius saw John coming home to supper. He was taking long fast strides. His head was high and he was smiling. She ran to meet him. "What is it, John?" she cried. "You look bursting with good news!"

"Guess who stopped to see me this afternoon?"

Before she could answer, he hurried on. "Amos Bosworth! He's on his way West! He's sold his stage lines, and he's going out to Illinois—to a little place called Grand Detour! A friend of his named Leonard Andrus has started a little town there—right where a river makes a big bend! There's water power aplenty! Andrus has already built a sawmill."

"Slow down a bit, John!" Demarius laughed. "I know what you're going to say next. They'll need a good blacksmith in Grand Detour."

John smiled at her. His eyes twinkled with excitement. "Yes, that's what Amos said. He urged me to go out there and see for myself. Do you think I should go, Demarius?"

"Yes, I do, John," she answered without hesitating. "You get so little here in return for your hard work. Out in the new lands the farmers will make a better living. So will a fine blacksmith named John Deere!"

166

The Precious Plow

CLANG! CLANG! The new sound rang out loud and clear on the early morning air around Grand Detour, Illinois.

The forest creatures were afraid. Never before had they heard a sound like that! Birds flew off across the river. Squirrels raced up tree trunks and chattered excitedly. A deer, drinking from Rock River, jerked up its head in alarm, then bounded into the forest.

Clang! Clang! The settlers of Grand Detour smiled as the first blows of John Deere's hammer on the anvil awakened them.

"Hear that, Martha?" one man asked his wife.

167

"That young blacksmith from Vermont is up and working with the sun!"

"Next to church bells, that's the sweetest ringing sound I ever did hear!" his wife exclaimed. "Now you won't have to make the forty-mile trip to get the horses shod."

"I can get some new bolts for the wagon, too. But first off, Martha, he can fix that broken leg on your big soap kettle!"

Across the river a farmer stopped milking his cow and turned to listen. "By cracky, Tom!" he called to his son, "as I live and breathe, that's a smith's hammer!"

"In Grand Detour, Pa?"

"I'd stake my life on it!" his father replied. "Now you hurry and finish this milking. I'm going to load the plow in the wagon. Maybe it would work better if that smith put some new iron strips over the wood."

Later that day, Amos Bosworth and Leonard

Andrus stood near the new forge, watching John work. Although the forge stood in the open, sweat glistened on the smith's forehead. The muscles in his big arms bulged as he brought his hammer down on the red-hot iron.

"Didn't I tell you, Leonard, that this young fellow was a wonder?" Amos spoke proudly. "Only been here two days, but before nightfall he'll have that shaft fixed and your sawmill will be running again!"

"Mighty lucky thing for us that he got here when he did," Major Andrus nodded. "Lots of folks were depending on lumber from the mill to get their homes built before snow flies."

"Well, you won't have to worry about that shaft breaking again. When John Deere welds something, it's as good as new!"

"He doesn't waste any time, either, does he?" Major Andrus said admiringly. "Why yesterday, soon as he heard how badly we needed that mill shaft repaired, he started carrying rocks up from the river to build this forge!"

"Yep, that's John Deere for you!" Amos chuckled. "Why, my wife couldn't even get him to stop for supper last night! He was set on getting those rocks bonded together with clay before night. And he did, too!"

All through that fall and winter of 1836, John was kept busy shoeing horses and oxen and repairing or making new iron tools for the settlers around Grand Detour. Inside the shop which he had built around his forge, farmers gathered to talk while they waited for a chain to be welded or an iron ring to be made.

As spring approached, the farmers brought in their plows to be sharpened or to have new strips of iron bolted to the wood.

"Don't know why I bother to get this fool plow fixed!" one farmer remarked bitterly as he dumped his plow on the floor of the shop.

"I know what you mean," another said gloomily. "I sure dread plowing time."

"If it's no better than last year, I'll sell my land and go back East!" said Lewis Crandall.

John let his hammer rest on the anvil and stared at Mr. Crandall. He could hardly believe his ears! He had seen Lewis's fine big farm lands just across Rock River.

"Why on earth would you leave your farm, with its rich black soil, Lewis?" he asked.

"I can't plow it!" Lewis Crandall's voice was loud. He slammed his fist on John's workbench. "Sure it's rich land. It would grow anything—if I could get a plow through it."

"A breaking plow can turn the sod the first time, but after that the soil sticks to our plows like glue!" another farmer explained.

"Why last spring, John," Mr. Crandall went on, "I hitched two teams of oxen to my plow. Those poor beasts nearly pulled their hearts

out, and mine, too! That prairie soil balls up and sticks to the moldboard like wet snow on your boots! You have to jerk the plow out of the furrows every few yards and clean it off with a wooden paddle! I tell you, John, it's more than a man can stand!"

"That it is!" another man agreed sadly. "I don't reckon I can plough more than twenty of my three hundred acres—even with a paddle and changing teams three or four times a day."

Another farmer spoke up. "I wrote and told my brother in New York State not to come here. Told him I guessed the good Lord never meant these prairie lands to grow our bread."

John's shoulders sagged as he looked out the door of his shop, off toward the river. Could it be possible that the farmers here in Illinois were going to fail, too? With all that rich farm land stretching away to the west, were these men going to have to take their families back to the small, rocky fields of the East? Just because they didn't have a plow that would turn the clinging earth and scour itself clean as it turned the soil?

As John went back to his forge, his heart was heavy for all the farmers who had so hopefully made the long journey to the new West. But his mind was busy, too. Here was a problem, a task, bigger and far more important than any he had ever had before. Could a plow be made that would solve this problem? Could he, John Deere, make a plow that would scour?

In the days that followed, although he went about his work as always, his thoughts were constantly on the plow. He studied the iron ones that were brought to his shop. Would a different curve help the gummy earth slide off the moldboard? What other material besides iron could a plow be made of?

John was thinking about these things as he

walked over to the sawmill one bright April morning in that year of 1837. He carried a letter he had written to Demarius. Major Andrus was going to the neighboring town of Dixon for supplies and would take the mail.

John had written some good news to Demarius. He had told her about their new home he was building on the street just west of his shop. It would be ready for her by summer. He was lonesome for his wife and children. Especially he wanted to see the new baby that must be nearly a month old now. John wondered if he had another pretty daughter, or if Francis now had a baby brother. He smiled as he thought how he would like another son.

As he entered the sawmill, sunlight flashed from something on the farther wall. A broken steel saw blade! John stopped and stared at the bright shining metal! His blue eyes began to sparkle with excitement. Steel! Here was the answer. A steel plow would polish as brightly as his mother's needles! Moist earth couldn't cling to that smooth surface!

"Major Andrus! Major Andrus!" he shouted.

The Major came running. "What's wrong, John? What is it?" he asked in alarm. Then he saw how happy the smith looked.

"It's steel, Major! That's the answer! I'll make a steel plow that will scour, if you'll sell me this broken saw blade."

"It's yours, John. Take it." Leonard Andrus laughed. "From the way you shouted, I thought your shop must be on fire!"

Word was soon carried through the little village of Grand Detour that the blacksmith was not shoeing any horses or repairing any tools. He was busy making a plow, a steel plow! Long after dark John worked by the light of his forge and a lantern. In the morning the settlers were awakened, not by the crowing of roosters, but

by the ring of John Deere's hammer on the anvil. They shook their heads.

"He's just wasting his time," scoffed some. "No plow is ever going to make a clean cut through this Illinois ground!"

"Well, I'll try anything," others said hopefully. "Maybe our blacksmith has a good idea."

"If Deere's plow doesn't work, we might as well give these prairies back to the Indians and buffaloes!" declared Lewis Crandall.

"How long before we'll know, Lewis?"

"Tomorrow, John says. I told him to bring his plow over to my place. If it will scour in that soil, it will work anywhere!"

The next morning was bright and clear. An air of excitement filled the little town. The main street had many more wagons than usual. Whole families had driven in early to watch the testing of the blacksmith's plow.

"By jove, it does shine!" someone exclaimed

178

when John finally came out the door of the smithy, carrying the new plow on his shoulder.

"But it's so small and light!" a man groaned.

"Say, John," one man called jokingly as the crowd followed the smith down to the river, "are you going to hitch two teams of oxen to that silver spoon you call a plow?"

"No. I told Lewis one horse would be enough," John answered good-naturedly. He put his plow into one of the rowboats.

"John is plumb daft!" exclaimed a tall farmer. "When two teams of oxen can't plow that ground, how in tarnation can one horse?"

"If John Deere says one horse will pull his plow, one horse will do it! I've never known him to be wrong yet!" Amos declared.

"I'll eat my Sunday hat if that little toy works," a tall farmer promised.

"If it does work, I'll have you eat it with my 'silver spoon' here!" John laughed.

The men rowed across the river. Then John carried the plow on his shoulder to the field where Lewis Crandall was waiting.

Soon the plow was hitched behind the horse. The joking stopped. Everyone was quiet as John set the cutting edge firmly into the rich moist ground. "You drive the horse, Lewis," he said. "I'll handle the plow."

"Giddap!" Lewis called, slapping the reins.

John's hands were firm on the smooth polished handles that he had made from sapling roots. The plowshare dug into the black earth. Three feet—six feet—twelve feet of straight furrow, and still the bright surface of the moldboard was clean!

The crowd of people following almost held their breath. On went the horse and plow. The earth fell away in a smooth, neat roll behind the easily moving plow.

"She scours! By thunder, she scours!" Lewis

Crandall shouted. He stopped the horse. John lifted the plow from the furrow. The sun gleamed from the bright, clean moldboard.

"It's clean! It's clean as a silver dollar!" the excited onlookers cried joyfully.

"Throw away your paddles, men! John Deere has made a plow that polishes itself!"

Lewis Crandall looked up from the plow and out across his beautiful valley farm land. Then he put his hand on the blacksmith's shoulder. In a husky voice he said, "Thanks, John. I can stay now. We can all stay and farm these lands, thanks to you!"

John felt happy and proud as he looked down at his precious plow, but he only answered, "Think I can make the next one better, Lewis, if I curve that moldboard a bit more."

Then everyone laughed as the tall farmer called out, "Give me your spoon, John. I'm ready and glad to eat my hat!"

182

Another
Birthday

"WAIT, FATHER! Let me go with you!"

John Deere was putting a plow into his wagon. Charles, his eight-year-old son, came running to join him. The boy climbed on the wagon wheel and touched the name on the wooden beam on the plow. "Where are you going to test this self-polisher?" he asked.

"I'm going to take it to some river bottom land. Did you finish your chores for Mother?"

"Yes, Father, I did. But I hurried so I could go with you!"

As the wagon jolted down the country road, John remembered the first time he had seen the sturdy lad sittting beside him. A few months after the testing of his first steel plow, he had heard that the wagons bringing his family from the East had reached Dixon. Amos Bosworth had gladly lent him a horse, and he had galloped out to meet them.

After he had hugged the older children, Demarius had handed the tiny, blanket-wrapped Charles to him. "Here, John," she had said with a tired smile. "Take your baby. He has cried all the way from Vermont!"

So little Charles had entered Grand Detour on horseback, held proudly against his father's broad shoulder. Young Charles still liked nothing better than to be with his father.

John Deere was no longer just a regular village blacksmith. Now he was also a manufacturer of plows. So many farmers had wanted his Self-Polisher that he had gone into partnership with Major Andrus. They had built a

184

large, two-story brick building where many more plows could be made. Last year, in 1843, they had turned out four hundred plows.

John often looked up from his forge to find Charles watching him. Sometimes he let the small boy pump the bellows, just as he had done for Captain Lawrence. He knew how important and grown-up it made a lad feel.

John was proud of his young son's interest in the making of plows. He smiled now as the boy asked, "Is this Self-polisher made from the steel that came across the ocean?"

"Yes, this one was made from English plate steel. But the steel had such a long journey over water that it rusted some. It wouldn't polish as smoothly as we wanted. That's why we got that big new grindstone that the horse turns. I'm going to test this moldboard now on that sticky bottom land to find out if it will scour as brightly as it should."

"Why do you have to send across the ocean for steel?" Charles asked.

"Because there is no steel mill in the United States that makes the kind we need for our plows," John answered thoughtfully. He was thinking that soon he would make a journey back to Pennsylvania to see if plow steel could be made for him in the Pittsburgh steel mills.

As he drove along, John Deere thought about other problems. Iron and coal had to be hauled forty miles into Grand Detour. Often the wagons got stuck on muddy roads. Taking new plows over these poor roads to farmers in other parts of Illinois was a hard job, too. Until last year, he had hoped the new railroad would come through Grand Detour. But now he knew it was going to miss the village.

The Mississippi River was only fifty miles west of Grand Detour. It was much easier to move loads in boats than in wagons. Should he move his plow factory and his family to a town beside the Mississippi?

He would talk it over with Demarius. Their happy little home in Grand Detour was really too small for their large famiy. Besides the five children born in Vermont, they now had little Emma, four years old, and baby Alice. If they moved, he would build Demarius a fine big house in their new town.

"Our Self-Polisher worked fine, didn't it, Father?" Charles said proudly, as they were going home. "I guess you make the best plow in the whole world!"

"Well, I keep trying to, anyway, son. Do you know, I just remembered something from a long time ago that may make our plows even better!"

"What is it?" Charles asked eagerly.

"When I was about your age, I used to polish my mother's needles by pushing them in and out of a little cloth strawberry that had a finely ground metal called emery powder inside it. That emery powder would polish those needles till they shone like silver!"

"And you're going to get some emery powder for your plows!" Charles guessed.

John smiled at his son's quick thinking. "You're right, Charles," he admitted, "but it won't be in a cloth strawberry. It will be on a wheel that turns—an emery wheel. Remember, son, if you set your mind to it, you can always find a way to make a thing better."

On a cold February night in 1882, a large group of people had gathered on a street at the foot of a steep hill in Moline, Illinois.

"Remember, folks," a man called, "we don't want him to hear a sound until we have the house surrounded! When I whistle, you shout 'Happy birthday' loud and clear! Don't forget what to say when he comes out!"

The crowd made their way up the snowy

street. They could see at the top of the hill the lighted windows of John Deere's beautiful large home overlooking the Mississippi River.

The people climbing the hill were office workers from his big farm implement factory, which was now called Deere & Company. As they struggled through the deep snow, they talked about the man they wanted to surprise.

One young man said to his older companion, "How long have you worked for Mr. Deere?"

"Why, I began working for John Deere the same year that his son Charles came into the company. That was twenty-four years ago!"

"Mr. Deere had a son that died, didn't he?"

"Yes. His name was Francis. He was only nineteen years old when he died. Mr. Deere had just moved his factory from Grand Detour. That was back in 1847—thirty five years ago!"

The younger man spoke again. "In the summer when I see all the corn and oats growing in the fields around here, I wonder what this part of the country would be like now, if John Deere hadn't made the farmers a steel plow!"

"It's hard to say. We just can't imagine this country without farms."

"I suppose at first most of the plows were sold here in the Midwest. Now we get orders for Deere plows from all over the world."

"Yes, John Deere's business grew rapidly because he always used only the best materials, and he improved his plows every year."

"I know Mr. Deere is seventy-eight years old today, but just yesterday when I was out in the forge shop, I saw him come in, go over to an anvil, take off his coat and hammer out a piece of hot iron!"

The older man laughed. "I guess John is prouder of having been a good blacksmith than of having had one of his plows win the International Award in France! The happiest look

190

I've ever seen on his face was once when he stopped to talk to me. He had just returned from a trip back to Vermont. He fairly beamed when he told me he had met a farmer back there who was still using a hayfork that John had made in his first blacksmith shop."

The younger man nodded. "Even though Mr. Deere is a rich man, he hasn't forgotten how hard it is to make a living sometimes. After my uncle had worked in the plow factory a long time, his eyes began to bother him. A foreman told him that he couldn't work there any more. Mr. Deere saw my uncle on the street and asked why he wasn't at work. When he heard what had happened, Mr. Deere was very angry. 'You go back and tell that man I sent you!' he said. 'As long as I live there'll be work for you in my factory!' My uncle still has a job there— but one that doesn't hurt his eyes."

"That's like John Deere. He looks out for

his workers," agreed the older man. "He's the most generous man I've ever known, too. He is always using his money to help people."

"He's a grand old gentleman, all right," replied the young man. "We're all proud to work for him. I hope he's really going to be surprised tonight."

The crowd of people had now reached the top of the hill. They had surrounded the front part of the house. A sharp whistle sounded.

"Happy birthday, John Deere! Happy birthday!" everyone shouted.

The door opened and tall straight, broad-shouldered man stood there. "Thank you, friends! Thank you!" he called. The light from the open door shone on his thick white hair. "Come in! Won't you all come in?"

But before they entered, they shouted again, "Happy birthday to our John Deere—the man who gave the world the steel plow!"

192

More About This Book

WHEN JOHN DEERE LIVED

1804   JOHN DEERE WAS BORN IN RUTLAND, VERMONT, FEBRUARY 7.

There were seventeen states in the Union.

Thomas Jefferson was President.

The population of the country was about 5,310,000.

1804–
1821   JOHN LIVED WITH HIS WIDOWED MOTHER AND ATTENDED SCHOOL.

Robert Fulton built the "Clermont," first practical steamboat, 1807.

The War of 1812 was fought, 1812-1815.

Florida was purchased from Spain, 1809.

1821–
1825   JOHN SERVED AS A BLACKSMITH APPRENTICE.

The Santa Fe Trail was completed, 1821.

The Monroe Doctrine was issued, 1823.

The Erie Canal was completed, 1825.

| 1825–
1836 | YOUNG DEERE WORKED AS A BLACKSMITH IN HIS OWN SHOPS AND FOR OTHERS. |

Peter Cooper built the first steam locomotive in the United States, 1830.

Cyrus McCormick invented the reaper, 1831.

Samuel Morse invented the telegraph, 1835.

| 1836–
1847 | DEERE WENT TO ILLINOIS, DEVELOPED A STEEL PLOW, AND BECAME A MANUFACTURER. |

American settlers reached Oregon, 1836.

A United States expedition to the southern oceans laid claim to Antarctica, 1840.

The Mexican War began, 1846.

The Mormons reached Great Salt Lake, 1847.

| 1847–
1886 | DEERE BUILT AND OPERATED HIS OWN COMPANY IN MOLINE, ILLINOIS. |

California became a state, 1850.

The War between the States was fought, 1861-1865.

Thomas Edison invented the phonograph, 1878, and the electric light bulb, 1879.

The first electric street railway in this country was operated in Baltimore, 1885.

194

1886 JOHN DEERE DIED IN MOLINE, ILLINOIS.

There were thirty-eight states in the Union.

Grover Cleveland was President.

The population of the country was about 59,150,000.

DO YOU REMEMBER?

1. How old was John Deere and where did he live at the beginning of the story?

2. What did John and Seth see when they went to the blacksmith shop with Uncle Amos?

3. How did John manage to get the old hornets' nest for his mother?

4. How did Mrs. Deere work to earn a living for her family of children?

5. How did John come to realize that all living creatures have feeling?

6. How did John celebrate his tenth birthday with the Miller family?

7. How did John help to make shoes for oxen in Captain Lawrence's blacksmith shop?

8. Why did the farmers in Vermont have to have their plows repaired frequently?

9. How did John become a blacksmith apprentice when he was seventeen years old?

10. What did young Deere first do to earn a living for himself and his family?

11. How did Deere come to move from Vermont to Grand Detour, Illinois?

12. Why were the farmers on the prairie unable to plow their land readily?

13. How did Deere make and test his first self-polishing plow?

14. Why did Deere decide to move his factory from Grand Detour to Moline?

IT'S FUN TO LOOK UP THESE THINGS

1. Why were blacksmith shops especially important in the early days of our country?

2. What were bellows in a blacksmith shop and how were they used?

3. Why do farmers need to plow ground in order to plant crops?

4. How are plows pulled today in most parts of our country?

5. What are the names of other important kinds of farm implements besides plows?

6. What are the most important farming regions of our country today?

INTERESTING THINGS YOU CAN DO

1. Draw a picture of an anvil similar to the one that John Deere used.

2. Explain why the land in the Midwest is often referred to as a prairie.

3. Make a list of crops which farmers raise widely in different parts of our country.

4. Find pictures of plows, reapers, and other farm implements for a display.

5. Name things once made in blacksmith shops that now are made in factories.

6. Draw a map to show where Deere settled and founded his company in Illinois.

7. Explain how Deere helped to settle the farmlands of our country.

OTHER BOOKS YOU MAY ENJOY READING

Cyrus McCormick: Farmer Boy, Lavinia Dobler. Trade and School Editions, Bobbs-Merrill.

Famous Inventors for Young People, Irmengarde Eberle. Dodd.

Man and His Tools, William A. Burns. Whittlesey.

Tractor Book, The, Margaret and Stuart Otto. Morrow.

Trails West and the Men Who Made Them, Edith Dorian and W. N. Wilson. Whittlesey.

Wheels, Edwin Tunis. World.

INTERESTING WORDS IN THIS BOOK

anvil (ăn′vĭl): special block of iron, on which metal is shaped

apprentice (ă prĕn′tĭs): young person bound by agreement to serve another person for a period of time to learn a trade

bellows (bĕl′ōz): device in blacksmith shop for blowing air

blacksmith (blăk′smĭth′): man who welds and makes things of iron

blast furnace: furnace used for making iron out of ore

boulder (bōl′dĕr) : large rounded rock

daft (dȧft) : foolish, crazy

dignified (dĭg′nĭ fīd) : lofty, noble

embarrass (ĕm băr′ăs) : upset, disturb

explorer (ĕks plōr′ĕr) : person who travels over little-known lands or seas for the purpose of discovery

flogging (flŏg′gĭng) : beating, as with whip or stick

forge (fôrj) : furnace or shop with a furnace where metal is heated and wrought

furrow (fûr′ō) : long narrow channel in the earth cut by a plow

implement (ĭm′plĕ mĕnt) : farm machine or tool

lieutenant (lū tĕn′ănt) : military officer next below a captain

mechanic (mĕ kăn′ĭk) : person who builds or repairs machines and tools

moldboard: curved iron or steel plate attached to a plowshare, which lifts, turns, and pulverizes the soil

musket (mŭs′kĕt) : hand firearm formerly carried by soldiers

pioneer (pī′ȯ nēr′) : early settler, also person who leads the way in developing something new, as in the field of science

postrider (pōst′rīd′ĕr) : messenger or mail carrier

prairie (prâr′ī) : large tract of level treeless land covered with coarse grass

pulpit (po͝ol′pĭt) : platform in a church from which a minister preaches

quinsy (kwĭn′zĭ) : severe inflammation of the throat, with swelling and fever

rolling mill: factory where iron is shaped into plates and bars

skillet (skĭl′ĕt) : frying pan

sleigh (slā) : carriage with runners for use on snow and ice

sloop (slo͞op) : usually a sailboat with one mast and a single headsail

spider (spī′dēr) : cast-iron frying pan with a handle

tannery (tăn′ēr ĭ) : place where hides are made into leather

tailor (tā′lēr) : person who makes clothes

whetstone (hwĕt′stōn′) : stone used for polishing or sharpening articles